INTRODUCTION TO NUMERICAL ANALYSIS

A Blaisdell Book in Pure and Applied Mathematics

CONSULTING EDITOR
George Springer, *Indiana University*

Introduction to Numerical Analysis

GERARD P. WEEG

University of Iowa

GEORGIA B. REED

Colorado State University

Blaisdell Publishing Company

A Division of Ginn and Company

WALTHAM, MASSACHUSETTS · TORONTO · LONDON

Preface

NUMERICAL APPROXIMATIONS to mathematical problems is an area of mathematics which has fascinated many of the great scholars, starting even with the ancient Greeks. This rich background has been recently compounded with an even greater growth due to the invention and use of digital computers. The result is an amount of knowledge of such proportions that the novice is often at a loss as to where to start studying the topic. Nevertheless, much of the material covered in numerical analysis should be made available to the student of the sciences as early as possible in his undergraduate program.

This book is intended to help in both of these problems, first by presenting a restricted set of topics, and second, by presenting those topics at a level of difficulty which should make the material available to the diligent student at the end of his sophomore year or at the beginning of his junior year in college. To develop these two points further, the authors are convinced that the eight topics presented in the book represent most of the areas in which numerical methods have been developed. From among the multitude of methods available in a given subject only one or two have been selected in each case. The selections have been made in such a way that the methods presented are first of all useful and secondly, representative of broad classes of techniques. Thus, if the material in this book is understood by the student and used, then as the student matures, the more complete books on numerical analysis become more easily available to him.

The authors have used this material at Michigan State University as a text for a one-term course on numerical analysis, with prerequisites of calculus and an introduction to differential equations. As a result, students in their second or third year of study have been in the majority in the classes. As part of the course, six sessions have been devoted to instruction in FORTRAN programming. With this background the students are expected to try various techniques on a computer with the emphasis being made upon the error analysis. Hand computation or work aided by desk calculators has not been stressed, primarily because the effect of errors is not easily observed with a small amount of time, computation, and data. The authors have believed that the student's time could better be spent on more important theoretical developments, with applications made on a digital computer.

The methods given in this book are not original, but they are immediately useful and represent broad areas of techniques. The topics have been pared down to a bare minimum so that the student (and teacher) can concentrate on these without having to determine which of a bewildering proliferation of methods to study.

Since this book draws its material from already tried and proven techniques, it must necessarily owe a debt to many numerical analysts. In particular the authors have been heavily influenced by two excellent books. The first is F. B. Hildebrand's *Introduction to Numerical Analysis*, McGraw-Hill Book Co. New York, 1956. The second is Kaiser S. Kunz's *Numerical Analysis*, McGraw-Hill Book Co. New York, 1957.

We also owe much to Professor L. W. Von Tersch, Director of the Computer Laboratory at Michigan State University, who made time available for us to proceed with this work. And as with all authors, we are greatly indebted to our respective spouses for all their inspiration, help, and encouragement. Finally, we thank Mrs. Lois Hoffmeister, who typed the original manuscript at Michigan State University, and Mrs. Elliene Goughnour, who typed revisions for the manuscript at the University of Iowa.

Gerard P. Weeg

Georgia B. Reed

Contents

CHAPTER 1

Errors in Numerical Computation

IN ANY COMPUTATION which uses a fixed number length or some finite approximation to a process the problem of errors is present. These errors generally are unavoidable, but they can usually be estimated so that end results can be assigned reasonable significance. This chapter describes the types of error which occur in numerical computation, and presents methods for determining how seriously the errors affect the end results.

1.1 Introductory Remarks

It is to be emphasized that the errors to be studied in this chapter are not blunders or mistakes, but rather are unavoidable results of numerical computations. What should be hoped for is that an upper bound for the total final error can be found. Further, it is to be hoped that alternate methods of attack for a given problem may be found so that possibly the total error by one method has a smaller upper bound than by other methods.

Numerical computation normally is carried out with the assistance of some kind of calculating device, be it paper and pencil, desk calculator, or a digital computer. All of these devices have in common the fact that a maximum number length is assumed, and that only a finite amount of time is available to perform a computation. Hence, given a number n, it is supposed in advance that n is composed of at most a given number of digits, say d digits. Furthermore, in the course of a computation, if results exceed d digits, the results will be shortened so as to have no more than d digits. Thus, two sources of error are already evident, namely, errors due to shortened initial data, and errors due to the use of "pseudo-arithmetic operations," that is, operations which approximate arithmetic operations.

Since only a finite amount of time can be allowed to elapse in the course of a computation, any process based on an infinite procedure must be truncated (cut off after a finite amount of computation). Thus, suppose the problem is to calculate sin x by use of the infinite series

$$\sin x = x - \frac{x^3}{3!} + \frac{x^5}{5!} - \frac{x^7}{7!} + \cdots + (-1)^{n+1} \frac{x^{2n-1}}{(2n-1)!} + \cdots. \quad (1.1.1)$$

After a finite amount of computation the sum of the first m terms, say, of the series in Equation 1.1.1 would have been calculated, that is, the quantity

$$s(x) = x - \frac{x^3}{3!} + \frac{x^5}{5!} - \frac{x^7}{7!} + \cdots + (-1)^{m+1} \frac{x^{2m-1}}{(2m-1)!}, \quad (1.1.2)$$

where $s(x)$ is used simply to provide a name for the sum on the right side of Equation 1.1.2. Then the difference sin $x - s(x)$ is the error if $s(x)$ is used as an approximation to sin x. This error is called the truncation error associated with $s(x)$ as an approximation for sin x or, simply, *truncation error*.

In the next three sections the three kinds of errors described above are examined. Once again, these errors are:
1. Errors due to shortened initial data.
2. Errors due to the use of pseudo-arithmetic operations.
3. Truncation error in the computational procedure.
Further, the accumulative effect of all these errors is discussed.

1.2 Errors Due to Shortened Initial Data

Errors which arise from shortening data and which come from the use of pseudo-operations are sometimes called *round-off* errors. However, it is beneficial to be more precise in this analysis of error, so that such broad terms will not be used.

The problem of shortening initial data arises, as was pointed out, by the need to use no more than a certain number of digits, say d digits, to represent any given number, say n. Thus, for example, if a desk calculator is used, the data used must not exceed ten or twelve digits usually, since that is as wide as most keyboards come. If a digital computer is used, again the data used must not exceed 35 or 39 binary digits on certain computers, or ten decimal digits on certain other computers. It is to be granted that by certain manipulations the number of allowable digits in a number can be doubled, tripled or more, but even when such has been done there is still some fixed maximum **number length** remaining. Hence the problem of shortening data is simply **postponed**, but not avoided.

The problem then can be given as follows: Suppose that in a computation no number can possess more than d digits in its representation. If a number, a, has more than d digits, how can a be represented in the computation? The answer, of course, is to replace a by a number, $\hat{a}$, where $\hat{a}$ is d digits long, and such that the error α, where

$$a - \hat{a} = \alpha, \tag{1.2.1}$$

is no greater than can be tolerated. Ordinarily $\hat{a}$ will be chosen as the most significant d digits of a, with some account made for the part of a being removed. But if a is an integer, $\hat{a}$ must have sufficient zeroes on its right end so as to put the first d digits of $\hat{a}$ in the same range as those of a. Then, however, $\hat{a}$ will be composed of more than d digits. To avoid this problem, numbers are scaled; that is, each number a is represented as a number b, of d digits, multiplied by some power of the radix (in the decimal number system the radix is 10).

EXAMPLE 1.2.1 In a certain computation the maximum number length is to be three digits. How can the following numbers be represented?

$$4090000$$
$$365$$
$$42.9$$
$$-0.000762$$

Solution: The representations are as follows.

$$4090000 = 409 \times 10^4$$
$$365 = 365 \times 10^0$$
$$42.9 = 42.9 \times 10^0$$
$$-0.000762 = -0.762 \times 10^{-3}$$

In the actual calculation the various powers of ten will not show up, but these powers will be accounted for in the way in which the computational results are obtained and interpreted. Thus, to multiply 4090000 by -0.000762, the numbers 409 and -0.762 would actually be used, with the knowledge that the result would have to be multiplied by 10^1.

There are two commonly used ways of shortening data; namely by truncation and by rounding. If a is a real number written in decimal notation, where $10^n \leq a < 10^{n+1}$, then

$$a = \sum_{i=0}^{n} a_i 10^i + \sum_{i=-1}^{-\infty} a_i 10^i, \tag{1.2.2}$$

where the a_i are selected from the digits 0 through 9. The first sum is the integer part of a, while the second sum is the fractional part of a. If a is in the range $-1 < a < 1$, it will be completely defined by the second sum in

Equation 1.2.2. It is more convenient to rewrite the representation of a as

$$a = \sum_{i=0}^{\infty} b_i 10^{n-i}, \tag{1.2.3}$$

where the b_i are selected from the digits 0 through 9.

For example, the number $100\pi = 314.1592653589\cdots$ is represented in the form of Equations 1.2.2 or 1.2.3 by observing that

$$100\pi = 3 \times 10^2 + 1 \times 10^1 + 4 \times 10^0 + 1 \times 10^{-1}$$
$$+ 5 \times 10^{-2} + 9 \times 10^{-3} + \cdots$$

so that

$$n = 2, a_2 = 3, a_1 = 1, a_0 = 4, a_{-1} = 1, a_{-2} = 5, a_{-3} = 9, \ldots$$

whereas

$$b_0 = 3, b_1 = 1, b_2 = 4, b_3 = 1, b_4 = 5, b_5 = 9, \ldots \;.$$

If the number a is to be shortened by truncation to a representation $\hat{a}$ having only d digits, then one selects

$$\hat{a} = b_0 10^n + b_1 10^{n-1} + \cdots + b_{d-1} 10^{n-d+1}. \tag{1.2.4}$$

That is, the d most significant digits of a are used to form $\hat{a}$. On the other hand, if a is shortened, by rounding, to a representation $\bar{a}$, of d digits, then

$$\bar{a} = b_0 10^n + b_1 10^{n-1} + \cdots + b_{d-1} 10^{n-d+1} \tag{1.2.5}$$

if

$$|b_d| < 5,$$

and

$$\bar{a} = b_0 10^n + b_1 10^{n-1} + \cdots + (b_{d-1} + 1) 10^{n-d+1} \tag{1.2.6}$$

if

$|b_d| \geq 5$ and $a > 0$. For $a < 0$, $(b_{d-1} + 1)$ is replaced by $(b_{d-1} - 1)$.

Let

$$\hat{\alpha} = a - \hat{a},$$
$$\bar{\alpha} = a - \bar{a}. \tag{1.2.7}$$

Hence

$$\hat{\alpha} = \sum_{i=d}^{\infty} b_i 10^{n-i} \tag{1.2.8}$$

and

$$\bar{\alpha} = \sum_{i=d}^{\infty} b_i 10^{n-i} \tag{1.2.9}$$

if $|b_d| < 5$, while

$$\bar{\alpha} = \mp 1 \times 10^{n-d+1} + \sum_{i=d}^{\infty} b_i 10^{n-1} \tag{1.2.10}$$

when $|b_d| \geq 5$ according as a is positive or negative. Hence, $|\hat{\alpha}| \leq 1 \times 10^{n-d+1}$. For example, when $b_i = 9$ for $i = d, d+1, \ldots$, then $\hat{\alpha} = 1 \times 10^{n-d+1}$. However, $|\bar{\alpha}| \leq 0.5 \times 10^{n-d+1}$, since if $|b_d| < 5$, then $\bar{\alpha}$ is at most $(49999 \cdots) \times 10^{n-d} = 5 \times 10^{n-d} = 0.5 \times 10^{n-d+1}$; but if $b_d \geq 5$, then $\bar{\alpha}$ is at least $-1 \times 10^{n-d+1} + 5 \times 10^{n-d} = -0.5 \times 10^{n-d+1}$.

Finally, $|\bar{\alpha}| \leq |\hat{\alpha}|$, so that the conclusion to be made is that numbers should be shortened by rounding rather than by truncation so as to minimize the unavoidable error.

EXAMPLE 1.2.2   Shortening 100π to five digits by truncation gives

$$\widehat{100\pi} = 314.15$$

while by rounding

$$\overline{100\pi} = 314.16.$$

The error

$$\hat{\alpha} = 100\pi - \widehat{100\pi} = 0.00926535 \cdots$$

while the error $\bar{\alpha}$ is

$$\bar{\alpha} = 100\pi - \overline{100\pi} = -0.00073464 \cdots.$$

Hence, $|\bar{\alpha}|$ is considerably less than $|\hat{\alpha}|$.

It is assumed in this book that if a number such as $a = \sum\limits_{i=0}^{\infty} b_i 10^{n-i}$ is to be represented by a number $\bar{a}$ with d *digits of precision*, then the error (henceforth written without the bar above) $\alpha = a - \bar{a}$ will be such that $|\alpha| \leq 0.5 \times 10^{n-d+1}$; that is, the error will be less than or equal to $\frac{1}{2}$ in the last digit position to be retained. Further, if a number, a, is to be represented by a number $\bar{a}$ which is to have m *decimal places of accuracy*, then $\alpha = a - \bar{a}$ is such that $|\alpha| \leq 0.5 \times 10^{-m}$.

EXAMPLE 1.2.3   Represent the number $a = -476.4932176$ by a number $\bar{a}$ with 6 digits of precision.

Solution: $\bar{a} = -476.493$. Notice that $\bar{a}$ can represent any number less than or equal to -476.4925 and greater than -476.4935.

EXAMPLE 1.2.4   Represent $a = -476.4932176$ by a number $\bar{a}$ with 6 decimal places of accuracy.

Solution: $\bar{a} = -476.493218$.

The error in the number due to rounding is usually magnified by arithmetic operations. Suppose that it is desired to operate with two numbers, a and b, which have been rounded to d places to become $\bar{a}$ and $\bar{b}$, where

$$a - \bar{a} = \alpha,$$
$$b - \bar{b} = \beta.$$

(1.2.11)

Then in place of the sum $a + b$ the sum $\bar{a} + \bar{b}$ is formed, where now

$$\bar{a} + \bar{b} = a + b - (\alpha + \beta). \tag{1.2.12}$$

Thus, the error in the representation of the sum $a + b$ has become the sum of the errors in $\bar{a}$ and $\bar{b}$. If α and β both have the same sign, the error has increased. Hence, since the error in $\bar{a}$ and $\bar{b}$ were both at most $\frac{1}{2}$ in the last place retained, the error in the sum representation now is at most 1 in that place.

EXAMPLE 1.2.5   How many decimal places of accuracy can be claimed in the sum

$$0.071 + 0.091 + 0.176 + 0.498 + 0.273$$
$$+ 0.001 + 1.456 + 1.001 + 4.000 + 0.171$$

if each summand is accurate to three decimal places?

Solution: Since each summand is accurate to three decimal digits, then each summand has a maximum error of 0.5×10^{-3}. The error in the sum then is at most $10 \times (0.5 \times 10^{-3}) = 5.0 \times 10^{-3} = 0.5 \times 10^{-2}$. Hence, no more than two decimal places of accuracy can be assumed.

It is easily seen that in subtracting two inaccurate numbers the result has an error which may be as great as the sum of the two original errors. Similarly, in multiplying $\bar{a}$ by $\bar{b}$ it is seen that

$$\bar{a}\bar{b} = (a - \alpha)(b - \beta)$$
$$= ab - (b\alpha + a\beta - \alpha\beta). \tag{1.2.13}$$

Thus the error in $\bar{a}\bar{b}$ is essentially $b\alpha + a\beta$ if α and β are small with respect to a and b. Likewise, when dividing $\bar{a}$ by $\bar{b}$, it is seen that

$$\frac{\bar{a}}{\bar{b}} = \frac{a - \alpha}{b - \beta} = (a - \alpha)(b - \beta)^{-1}. \tag{1.2.14}$$

Assuming that $\left| \dfrac{\beta}{b} \right| < 1$, $(b - \beta)^{-1}$ can be expanded to give

$$\frac{\bar{a}}{\bar{b}} = \frac{a - \alpha}{b}\left[1 + \frac{\beta}{b} + \left(\frac{\beta}{b}\right)^2 + \left(\frac{\beta}{b}\right)^3 + \cdots\right]$$
$$= \frac{a}{b} - \left(\frac{\alpha}{b} - \frac{a\beta}{b^2} + \cdots\right). \tag{1.2.15}$$

Hence, the error in $\bar{a}/\bar{b}$ is approximately $\alpha/b - a\beta/b^2$.

A more easily remembered result concerning the accumulative effect of rounding errors in multiplication and division can be obtained if relative errors are used. The relative error in an approximation $\bar{a}$ to the number a will be given as $\dfrac{\alpha}{\bar{a}}$ where $a - \bar{a} = \alpha$. This is somewhat different from the definition often encountered, but has the advantage that the only quantities used in the relative error are those which are available, namely, $\bar{a}$ and α. If α is not known exactly, it is usually the case that a good upper bound for $|\alpha|$ is known. It should be observed that since

$$a = \bar{a} + \alpha, \tag{1.2.16}$$

then

$$a = \bar{a}\left(1 + \frac{\alpha}{\bar{a}}\right). \tag{1.2.17}$$

Hence, if a can be written in the form

$$a = \bar{a}(1 + \epsilon), \tag{1.2.18}$$

then ϵ is the relative error in $\bar{a}$, that is, $\epsilon = \dfrac{\alpha}{\bar{a}}$.

In the case of multiplication, it follows that

$$ab = \bar{a}\left(1 + \frac{\alpha}{\bar{a}}\right)\bar{b}\left(1 + \frac{\beta}{\bar{b}}\right)$$

$$= \bar{a}\bar{b}\left(1 + \frac{\alpha}{\bar{a}} + \frac{\beta}{\bar{b}} + \frac{\alpha\beta}{\bar{a}\bar{b}}\right). \tag{1.2.19}$$

As a result, the relative error in $\bar{a}\bar{b}$ is $\dfrac{\alpha}{\bar{a}} + \dfrac{\beta}{\bar{b}} + \dfrac{\alpha\beta}{\bar{a}\bar{b}}$. Assuming that $\dfrac{\alpha\beta}{\bar{a}\bar{b}}$ is much smaller than either $\dfrac{\alpha}{\bar{a}}$ or $\dfrac{\beta}{\bar{b}}$, then the relative error in the product $\bar{a}\bar{b}$ is approximately the *sum of the relative errors of $\bar{a}$ and $\bar{b}$*. A similar statement can be made concerning division.

The method of analysis of error in arithmetic operations due to inaccurate data gives little help in determining the effect of inaccurate data upon more complicated mathematical expressions. That is, if $a_1, a_2, a_3, \ldots, a_n$ are the arguments of a function f, which are known only approximately as $\bar{a}_1, \bar{a}_2, \bar{a}_3, \ldots, \bar{a}_n$, respectively, where

$$a_i = \bar{a}_i + \alpha_i, \tag{1.2.20}$$

what is the error in using $f(\bar{a}_1, \bar{a}_2, \bar{a}_3, \ldots, \bar{a}_n)$ to approximate $f(a_1, a_2, a_3, \ldots, a_n)$? The error, of course, is

$$\delta = f(a_1, a_2, a_3, \ldots, a_n) - f(\bar{a}_1, \bar{a}_2, \bar{a}_3, \ldots, \bar{a}_n). \tag{1.2.21}$$

If f can be expanded in a convergent Taylor's series about $(\bar{a}_1, \bar{a}_2, \bar{a}_3, \ldots, \bar{a}_n)$ (see Appendix B), then

$$f(a_1, a_2, a_3, \ldots, a_n) = f(\bar{a}_1, \bar{a}_2, \bar{a}_3, \ldots, \bar{a}_n) + \sum_{i=1}^{n} \frac{\partial f}{\partial a_i} \alpha_i$$

$$+ \frac{1}{2} \sum_{i=1}^{n} \sum_{j=1}^{n} \frac{\partial^2 f}{\partial a_i \, \partial a_j} \alpha_i \alpha_j + \cdots. \qquad (1.2.22)$$

Ignoring terms of higher degree than the first in the α_i,

$$\delta = f(a_1, a_2, a_3, \ldots, a_n) - f(\bar{a}_1, \bar{a}_2, \bar{a}_3, \ldots, \bar{a}_n) \approx \sum_{i=1}^{n} \frac{\partial f}{\partial a_i} \alpha_i. \qquad (1.2.23)$$

EXAMPLE 1.2.6   If π is approximated by $\bar{\pi} = 3.1416$, how many decimal places of accuracy are there in using $\sqrt{\bar{\pi}} = 1.772455$ to approximate $\sqrt{\pi}$?

Solution: Since $\pi = \bar{\pi} + \epsilon$, where $|\epsilon| \leq 1 \times 10^{-5}$, then from Equation 1.2.23

$$|\delta| = |\sqrt{\pi} - \sqrt{\bar{\pi}}| \approx \frac{1 \times 10^{-5}}{2\sqrt{\bar{\pi}}} \approx \frac{1 \times 10^{-5}}{3.544910} \approx 0.3 \times 10^{-5}.$$

As a result, the error in using $\sqrt{\bar{\pi}}$ to represent $\sqrt{\pi}$ is less than the error in using $\bar{\pi}$ to represent π.

EXAMPLE 1.2.7   If $\theta = \bar{\theta} + \epsilon$, what is the error in using $\sin \bar{\theta}$ to represent $\sin \theta$?

Solution: Using Equation 1.2.23, $\delta = \sin \theta - \sin \bar{\theta} \approx \epsilon \cos \bar{\theta}$.

Thus, since $|\cos \bar{\theta}| \leq 1$, $|\delta| \leq |\epsilon|$.

Exercise

If $a = \bar{a} + \alpha$, how does the size of $\bar{a}$ affect the error in using $\sqrt{\bar{a}}$ to represent $\sqrt{a}$?

1.3   Errors Due to the Use of Pseudo-Arithmetic Operations

By a pseudo-arithmetic operation is meant some operation which produces the same result as a corresponding arithmetic operation to within a certain unavoidable error.

The pseudo-operations of concern with a desk calculator or with a digital computer are the counterparts of $+$, $-$, $\times$, $\div$ of usual arithmetic in which every result must be a number with at most d digits in it, for some d. Hence, some loss of accuracy will occur.

Let $\oplus$, $\ominus$, $\otimes$, and $\oslash$ represent the pseudo-operations corresponding respectively to $+$, $-$, $\times$, $\div$; then addition of two numbers of the same sign, each with d digits, using $\oplus$, may result in $d + 1$ digits so that some digit must be discarded. This difficulty and the corresponding one for $\ominus$ can be circumvented by requiring that the original data be scaled so that no sum exceeds d digits. However, such is not the case with $\otimes$ and $\oslash$. If

$$a = \sum_{i=0}^{d-1} a_i \times 10^{n-i} \qquad (1.3.1)$$

and

$$b = \sum_{i=0}^{d-1} b_i \times 10^{m-i}, \qquad (1.3.2)$$

then

$$ab = \sum_{i=0}^{2(d-1)} c_i \times 10^{m+n-i}, \qquad (1.3.3)$$

where the c_i are coefficients which can be found by multiplying a and b. But

$$a \otimes b = \sum_{i=0}^{d-1} c_i \times 10^{m+n-i} \qquad (1.3.4)$$

with the result that

$$ab - a \otimes b = \sum_{i=d}^{2(d-1)} c_i \times 10^{m+n-i}. \qquad (1.3.5)$$

For appropriate values of a and b, $ab - a \otimes b$ could be almost $1 \times 10^{m+n-d+1}$. That is, the error due to using $a \otimes b$ could be almost 1 in the last place of $a \times b$ or, if a rounded multiplication is used, as much as 0.5 in the last digit of $a \times b$ retained. A similar result can be stated for $\oslash$.

The result of the errors discussed in Sections 2 and 3 can now be connected. In a digital computer, both pseudo-operations and rounded numbers are involved, so that a double error is to be found. Thus, suppose ab is to be formed. If a and b are represented in the computer by $\bar{a}$ and $\bar{b}$ respectively, where

$$\begin{aligned} a - \bar{a} &= \alpha, \\ b - \bar{b} &= \beta, \end{aligned} \qquad (1.3.6)$$

then the number formed in the computer is $\bar{a} \otimes \bar{b}$. Define

$$\begin{aligned} ab - \bar{a}\bar{b} &= \gamma, \\ \bar{a}\bar{b} - \bar{a} \otimes \bar{b} &= \delta. \end{aligned} \qquad (1.3.7)$$

Observe that in the first equation both products are true, not pseudo-multiplications. In the second equation δ is the difference between the result of true multiplication and a pseudo-multiplication. Hence, the error γ is to be found by Equation 1.2.13, namely $\gamma = b\alpha + a\beta - \alpha\beta$. The error δ is of the form presented in Equation 1.3.5, so that $|\delta|$ may be nearly 1 in the last digit retained in the pseudo-multiplication. Using the definitions given in Equation 1.3.7,

$$ab - \bar{a} \otimes \bar{b} = (ab - \bar{a}\bar{b}) + (\bar{a}\bar{b} - \bar{a} \otimes \bar{b}) = \gamma + \delta. \qquad (1.3.8)$$

Hence, the error in the pseudo-operation and the round-off error accumulate to produce a conceivably greater error. As a result, if it is possible to make γ or δ small, this should indeed be done. In particular, using a computing device which permits d digit numbers (that is, the pseudo-operations operate on d digit numbers and produce d digit results) while certain data is accurate only to m digits, where $m < d$, the numbers should be scaled, if possible, so that each number is d digits long. For then the error due to the pseudo-operations may be considerably smaller than the error in the original data.

EXAMPLE 1.3.1   For convenience in this example, suppose that a computing device is to be used which accepts only 4 digit fractional numbers and which produces only 4 digit fractional numbers. Suppose the numbers 4.73 and 0.016 are obtained by a method of observation, in which the first two nonzero digits are accurate but in which the third digit is probably in error by as much as 5 either way. Form the pseudo-product of the two numbers, and determine the error in the result.

Solution: Scale both numbers, the first by 10^{-1} and the second by 10^1. The number 4.73 is thus represented by 0.4730, since the computing device requires 4 digit fractions. The second number is scaled up to 0.1600 so that the errors due to pseudo-multiplication occur farther away from the significant digits. It should be observed that the maximum error in 0.4730 is $\pm 5 \times 10^{-3}$ while the maximum error in 0.16 is $\pm 5 \times 10^{-2}$.

Let a and b be the true numbers approximated by 4.73 and 0.016 respectively. Then scale a and b in the same way that their representations were scaled, namely, replace a by $a \times 10^{-1}$ and b by $b \times 10$. Then

$$\gamma = (a \times 10^{-1})(b \times 10) - (0.473)(0.16).$$

Now it is known that 0.473 is in error by at most $\pm 5 \times 10^{-3}$ while 0.16 is in error by at most $\pm 5 \times 10^{-2}$. Hence, γ is at most

$$|(a \times 10^{-1})(5 \times 10^{-2})| + |(b \times 10)(5 \times 10^{-3})| + |(5 \times 10^{-2})(5 \times 10^{-3})|.$$

But $|a \times 10^{-1}| < 0.5$ and $|b \times 10| < 0.2$, so that

$$|\gamma| \leq 2.5 \times 10^{-2} + 1.0 \times 10^{-3} + 2.5 \times 10^{-4}.$$

Next

$$\delta = (0.4730)(0.16) - (0.473) \otimes (0.16).$$

But $|\delta|$ may be as much as 1 in the last place retained in the pseudo-multiplication. Hence $|\delta| \leq 10^{-4}$. As a result, the absolute value of $\gamma + \delta$ in forming the product ab, using inaccurate values in place of a and b and using pseudo-multiplications, is bounded by

$$|\gamma| + |\delta| \leq 2.5 \times 10^{-2} + 10^{-3} + 2.5 \times 10^{-4} + 10^{-4}$$

$$= (250 + 10 + 2.5 + 1) \times 10^{-4}$$

$$= 263.5 \times 10^{-4}$$

$$= 0.2635 \times 10^{-1}.$$

In this case, the error due to pseudo-multiplication is negligible in the total error, since the numbers used were much larger than their accuracy alone would have dictated.

1.4 Truncation Error in the Computational Procedure

Since digital computing devices, be they desk calculators or large electronic computers, can perform only the fundamental arithmetical operations of addition, subtraction, multiplication and division, the only mathematical quantity which can be calculated by their use is a rational fraction, that is, the quotient of two polynomials. It is fortunately the case that most functions commonly encountered can be approximated by rational fractions. However, the fact that these are only approximations should be emphasized. Thus, for example, the integral $\int_a^b f(x)\,dx$ can be approximated (by Simpson's rule) by

$$\frac{h}{3}(f_0 + 4f_1 + 2f_2 + 4f_3 + \cdots + 4f_{n-1} + f_n),$$

where n is chosen large enough to produce an error term which is acceptable. However, regardless of the size of n, the error is generally present. Such an error, due to the use of a formula which replaces an infinite process by a finite approximation, is called *truncation error*. In the succeeding chapters various approximate methods of performing certain processes are discussed. Associated with each method is a truncation error analysis. The student should view the error analysis as the most important part of each method, since that analysis generally determines the parameters of the approximation. Thus, for example, in Simpson's rule above, the student will learn that the error analysis determines the size of h and the value of n. However, the precise truncation error for a given application is not usually available, but instead an upper bound of the absolute value of the truncation error as small as possible is found.

1.5   The Accumulative Effect of Errors

If in a computation any number, a, is produced (or introduced as an input datum) with an error α, that error will generally propagate itself throughout the entire computation. What is even worse is that the introduction of an error in an iterative process may change the basic convergence of the process. For example, if a certain sequence $x_0, x_1, x_2, x_3, \ldots$, in which x_i depends upon all the previous iterates, converges to a certain value, x, the question arises as to what can be said about that sequence if one iterate acquires an error. That the sequence converges is left in doubt. In any case, the accumulation of the error must be estimated to determine the accuracy of the end result.

As has already been noted, the major attention in this book is directed to the error analysis associated with each numerical method investigated. Error analyses are not usually easy and in fact very often require some sophisticated computation. However, numerical methods without some determination of the errors involved are of questionable usefulness.

CHAPTER 2

The Real Roots of an Equation

ONE OF THE IMPORTANT PROBLEMS in mathematics, and in engineering and science as well, is that of finding roots of equations. The subject, Theory of Equations, is devoted to this problem. However, the concern in this book is not so much with the theory as covered there as it is with finding numerical values of the roots.

There are many methods available for finding the real roots of the equation $f(x) = 0$, where $f(x)$ is any piecewise continuous function of x. This chapter deals with only a few of these many possible methods.

All the methods discussed in this chapter depend, as indeed do most of the methods possible, on first finding a rough approximation to the root and then using the particular method to determine a sequence of successive approximations which converge to the desired root.

2.1 A Useful Theorem

A theorem which is useful in locating an approximate value of a root, as well as being a basis for one of the iterative methods discussed later, is the following:

THEOREM 2.1.1   If $f(x)$ is a real function, continuous in an interval (a, b), and if, for x_1 and x_2 values of x in this interval, $f(x_1)$ and $f(x_2)$ have opposite signs, then there is at least one real root of $f(x) = 0$ between $x = x_1$ and $x = x_2$.

EXAMPLE 2.1.1   Make use of Theorem 2.1.1 to find an approximate value of a positive real root of the equation

$$f(x) = x^2 - 2 = 0.$$

Solution: Here $f(x)$ is a polynomial and it can be verified by the student that a polynomial is continuous for all values of x. Thus the continuity required by Theorem 2.1.1 is assured. Since $f(0) = -2$, $f(1) = -1$, and $f(2) = +2$, by Theorem 2.1.1 there is a root of this equation between $x = 1$ and $x = 2$. Also since $f(1.5) = 0.25$, this root lies between $x = 1$ and $x = 1.5$. The location of this root may be approached even more closely by observing that $f(1.4) = -0.04$, showing that the root is actually between $x = 1.4$ and $x = 1.5$.

Exercises

1. If $f(x)$ satisfies the conditions of Theorem 2.1.1 for x_1 and x_2, a well-known computer "folk-technique" (that is, one which all computer programmers use but which is never documented) is the method of "binary-chopping." In this method $x_3 = \frac{1}{2}(x_1 + x_2)$ is formed. Thus x_3 replaces x_i if $f(x_3)$ and $f(x_i)$ are of the same sign, for $i = 1$ or 2. A new value of x_3 is formed, and the process continued.

Use the binary chopping method to approximate the positive root of $x^3 - 3 = 0$, to an accuracy of 2^{-4}.

2. Show that the nth value of x_3 formed as above differs from the root of $f(x) = 0$ by at most 2^{-n} if there is but a single root of the equation between x_1 and x_2, provided x_1 and x_2 differ by at most 1.

2.2 Graphical Method of Finding an Approximate Value of a Real Root

One of the simplest and most common methods for locating an approximate value for a real root of the equation $f(x) = 0$ is to make a rough plot of the function

$$y = f(x) \tag{2.2.1}$$

and observe where this plot crosses the x-axis.

It is sometimes advantageous to write the equation $f(x) = 0$ as

$$f_1(x) = f_2(x). \tag{2.2.2}$$

Then the two equations

$$y_1 = f_1(x) \quad \text{and} \quad y_2 = f_2(x) \tag{2.2.3}$$

may be plotted separately. The abscissas of their intersection points are the values of roots of $f(x) = 0$.

For the purpose of locating a root it is usually necessary to make only a rough sketch to locate the root approximately. More points may then be plotted in the neighborhood of the approximate root to find a closer approximation.

In making such a rough plot, it is helpful to examine the function for such information as: the limiting characteristics as $x \to \infty$ and $x \to -\infty$; the y-intercepts; the values of x at which $f(x)$ is undefined; and, in case of Equations 2.2.3, the x-intercepts, if possible.

EXAMPLE 2.2.1   Find an approximate root of the equation $f(x) = x^3 - 3 = 0$ graphically.

Solution: Examination of the equation $y = x^3 - 3$ shows
(1) $x = 0$, $y = -3$,
(2) $x < 0$, $y < 0$; therefore no real negative root,
(3) as $x \to \infty$, $y \to \infty$ and as $x \to -\infty$, $y \to -\infty$,
(4) $x = 1$, $y = -2$; $x = 2$, $y = +8$; hence there is at least one real root between $x = 1$ and $x = 2$,
(5) $x < 2$, $y < 0$ and increasing; hence there is no real root larger than $x = 2$.
It is necessary to plot the function only in a region near $x = 2$. The graph shows that a root is very near $x = 1.5$; hence $x = 1.5$ would be a possible

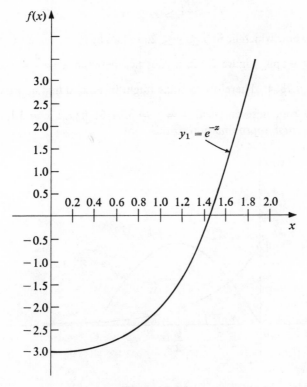

FIGURE 2.2.1

first approximation to the real root. Further examination shows that for $x = 1.4$, $y = -0.256$ and $x = 1.5$, $y = +0.375$. Hence $x = 1.45$ would be a better first approximation. Since no other root appears in this plot, it is assumed that there is only one real root for the equation. That such is indeed the case is shown in Section 2.3.

EXAMPLE 2.2.2 Find approximate values for the real roots of the equation

$$e^{-x} - \sin x = 0$$

graphically, for $0 \leq x \leq 2\pi$.

Solution: Let

$$y_1 = e^{-x} \quad \text{and} \quad y_2 = \sin x.$$

Since $y_1 = e^{-x}$ is such that

$$x < 0, \qquad y_1 > +1,$$
$$x > 0, \qquad 0 < y_1 < 1,$$

and

$$-1 \leq y_2 \leq +1,$$

all of the roots which lie in $0 \leq x \leq 2\pi$ in fact lie in the region $0 \leq x \leq \pi$. From the graph, Figure 2.2.2, a root lies between $x = \dfrac{\pi}{6} = 0.5236$ and $x = \dfrac{\pi}{4} = 0.7854$. Therefore $x = 0.6$ might be a good first approximation. A second root lies very near $x = \pi = 3.1416$; hence $x = 3.1$ might be taken as a first approximation to this root.

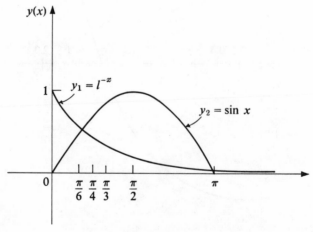

FIGURE 2.2.2

2.3 Some Special Properties of Polynomials

Although the methods of solution of the equation

$$f(x) = 0 \qquad (2.3.1)$$

discussed in this chapter are in no way dependent on $f(x)$ being a polynomial, polynomials occur frequently and are of sufficient importance to justify special attention.

One property of polynomials which is useful in finding roots as well as in many other situations may be stated as follows.

Property 2.3.1 If a polynomial, $P_n(x)$, of degree n is divided by $x - a$, the result is a quotient, which is a polynomial of degree $n - 1$, and a remainder R, such that $R = P_n(a)$. If $P_n(a) = R = 0$, a is a root of $P_n(x) = 0$ and $x - a$ is a factor of $P_n(x)$.

For, if

$$P_n(x) = (x - a)Q(x) + R, \qquad (2.3.2)$$

where R is a constant,* then if $x = a$,

$$P_n(a) = 0 \cdot Q(a) + R \qquad (2.3.3)$$

or

$$P_n(a) = R. \qquad (2.3.4)$$

The actual division of $P_n(x)$ by $x - a$ may be simplified by the well-known process of *synthetic division*. Synthetic division is performed as follows:

(1) Write the number a and the coefficients of $P_n(x)$ in order, as for an ordinary division, omitting the x's, but including zeroes as the coefficients of powers of x which do not appear in $P_n(x)$.

(2) Multiply the coefficient of x^n by a and add to the next coefficient.

(3) Multiply the result of this addition by a and add to the next coefficient.

(4) Repeat for all coefficients. The result of the last addition is $R = P_n(a)$.

EXAMPLE 2.3.1   Use synthetic division to find the values of $y = x^3 - 3$ for $x = 2$, $x = 1.4$ and $x = 1.5$ (see Examples 2.2.1).

Solution

$$
\begin{array}{rrrr|l}
1 & 0 & 0 & -3 & \underline{\;2\;} \\
  & 2 & 4 & 8 & \\
\hline
1 & 2 & 4 & 5 = P_3(2) &
\end{array}
\qquad
\begin{array}{rrrr|l}
1 & 0 & 0 & -3 & \underline{\;1.4\;} \\
  & 1.4 & 1.96 & 2.744 & \\
\hline
1 & 1.4 & 1.96 & -0.256 = P_3(1.4) &
\end{array}
$$

$$
\begin{array}{rrrr|l}
1 & 0 & 0 & -3 & \underline{\;1.5\;} \\
  & 1.5 & 2.25 & 3.375 & \\
\hline
1 & 1.5 & 2.25 & 0.375 = P_3(1.5) &
\end{array}
$$

* That $P_n(x)$ can be so expressed is demonstrated, for example, in G. Birkhoff and S. MacLane, *A Survey of Modern Algebra*, New York; Macmillan Company, 1953, pp. 69–70.

The preceding example illustrates one of the ways in which synthetic division is useful, that is in locating roots of polynomial equations or approximations to such roots.

A second property of polynomials is the following.

Property 2.3.2 If $Q(x)$ is the quotient of $P_n(x)$ divided by $x - a$, then division of $Q(x)$ by $x - a$ gives a remainder $R_1 = P'_n(a)$.

This property may be proved as follows: if

$$P_n(x) = (x - a)Q(x) + R, \tag{2.3.5}$$

then

$$P'_n(x) = (x - a)Q'(x) + Q(x), \tag{2.3.6}$$

so that

$$P'_n(a) = Q(a). \tag{2.3.7}$$

But $Q(a)$ is precisely the remainder if $Q(x)$ is divided by $x - a$.

Since the coefficients of $Q(x)$ are found in the third line of the synthetic division of $P_n(x)$ by a, then synthetic division of the third line (omitting R) by a gives a fifth line, the last number of which is $R_1 = Q_1(a) = P'_n(a)$.

EXAMPLE 2.3.2 Find the value of $P_4(x)$ and $P'_4(x)$ at $x = 2$ if $P_4(x) = x^4 + 3x^3 - 2x^2 + 5x - 10$.

Solution

$$
\begin{array}{rrrrr|l}
1 & 3 & -2 & 5 & -10 & \underline{\,2} \\
  & 2 & 10 & 16 & 42 & \\
\hline
1 & 5 & 8 & 21 & 32 = P_4(2) \\
  & 2 & 14 & 44 & \\
\hline
1 & 7 & 22 & 65 = P'_4(2) \\
\end{array}
$$

A further property of polynomials can be given as follows.

Property 2.3.3 Let $P_n(x)$ be a polynomial, with the coefficient of the highest power of x positive. If synthetic division of this polynomial by a positive number, a, results in all non-negative numbers, then $P_n(x) = 0$ has no real root larger than a. Also, if $P_n(-x)$ is formed and rewritten, if necessary, so that the leading coefficient is positive, and if synthetic division by a positive number, b, results in all non-negative numbers, $P_n(x) = 0$ has no real root less than $-b$. An alternative to this last rule is: if the signs of the result of dividing $f(x)$ by a negative number, $-b$, are alternating, $P_n(x) = 0$ has no real root smaller than $-b$.

This property is useful in locating upper and lower bounds to roots of a polynomial.

Note that to change $P_n(x)$ to $P_n(-x)$ it is necessary only to change the sign of all odd powers of x in the polynomial. Also note that the change of the coefficient of x^n from negative to positive involves multiplication of $P_n(x)$ by -1 and does not alter the roots of $P_n(x) = 0$.

EXAMPLE 2.3.3   Given the polynomial $P_3(x) = x^3 - 3x^2 - 10x + 24$, show that all real roots, r_i, of $P_3(x) = 0$ lie in the region $-4 < r_i < 5$.

Solution: Perform synthetic division by 5; thus

$$
\begin{array}{rrrr|r}
1 & -3 & -10 & 24 & \underline{5} \\
  & 5 & 10 & 0 & \\
\hline
1 & 2 & 0 & 24 &
\end{array}
$$

This results in all non-negative coefficients; hence there is no real 0 of $P_3(x)$ larger than 5.

Also, $P_3(-x) = -x^3 - 3x^2 + 10x + 24$. Synthetic division of $-P_3(-x)$ by $+4$ gives the following.

$$
\begin{array}{rrrr|r}
1 & 3 & -10 & -24 & \underline{4} \\
  & 4 & 28 & 72 & \\
\hline
1 & 7 & 18 & 48 &
\end{array}
$$

The all non-negative coefficients indicate, by Property 2.3.3, that there are no real roots of $P_3(x) = 0$ less than -4.

The same information about $x = -4$ could have been obtained by synthetic division of $P_3(x)$ by -4.

$$
\begin{array}{rrrr|r}
1 & -3 & -10 & 24 & \underline{-4} \\
  & -4 & +28 & -72 & \\
\hline
1 & -7 & 18 & -48 &
\end{array}
$$

Since the signs of the numbers in the third line alternate, then no root of $P_3(x) = 0$ can be less than -4.

EXAMPLE 2.3.4   Given the polynomial

$$P_3(x) = x^3 + 9x^2 + 26x + 24,$$

show that $x = -1$ is an upper bound on the real roots of $P_3(x) = 0$.

Solution: Property 2.3.3 gives conditions which guarantee a positive upper bound or a negative lower bound, but not conditions on a negative upper bound. However, inspection of the given function shows that synthetic division by any non-negative number gives all positive results; hence there are no positive real roots of $P_3(x) = 0$; that is, $x = 0$ is an upper bound. Synthetic division by -1 yields the following.

$$
\begin{array}{rrrr|r}
1 & 9 & 26 & 24 & \underline{-1} \\
  & -1 & -8 & -18 & \\
\hline
1 & 8 & 18 & 6 &
\end{array}
$$

Hence $P_3(-1) = 6$.

Since the third line is composed of positive numbers only, then if -1 is replaced by a negative number nearer zero, the entries in the third line will be even larger positive numbers and $f(x) > 6$ for $-1 < x < 0$; that is there is no zero of $P_3(x)$ in the interval $-1 \leq x < 0$ and $x = -1$ is in fact an upper bound on the roots of $P_3(x) = 0$.

It should be noted that the conditions given in Property 2.3.3 are sufficient but not necessary. For example, a number, n, may be larger than the largest zero of the polynomial in question without giving rise to non-negative coefficients on synthetic division.

EXAMPLE 2.3.5   The polynomial $P_3(x) = x^3 - 9x^2 + 26x - 24$ has zeros $x = 2$, $x = 3$ and $x = 4$. Show by synthetic division by $+5$ that the condition for an upper bound is not a necessary condition.

Solution: Synthetic division of the polynomial by $+5$ yields

$$
\begin{array}{rrrr|l}
1 & -9 & 26 & -24 & \underline{5} \\
  & 5 & -20 & 30 & \\
\hline
1 & -4 & 6 & 6 &
\end{array}
$$

and hence it is not apparent from this that $x = +5$ is in fact an upper bound on the real zeros of the given polynomial.

Exercises

1. Suppose that $x = a$ is a double root of the polynomial equation $P(x) = 0$. Then $P(x) = (x - a)^2 Q(x)$, where $Q(x)$ is a polynomial such that $Q(a) \neq 0$. Show that $\dfrac{d}{dx} P(x)$ also vanishes at $x = a$.

2. Show that for the polynomial in Exercise 1 the curve $y = P(x)$ touches the x-axis at $x = a$ but does not cross it.

3. Suppose that the polynomial $P(x)$ with real coefficients has the complex zero $a + bi$, where a and b are real numbers. Show that $P(x) = [(x - a)^2 + b^2]Q(x)$ for a polynomial $Q(x)$ which does not vanish at $x = a + bi$, assuming that $a + bi$ is not a repeated zero.

4. Plot the curve $y = P(x)$ for the polynomial of Exercise 3 in the vicinity of $x = a$, for $Q(x)$ increasing at a; decreasing at a; inflecting at a.

5. If synthetic division of a polynomial $P_n(x)$ by a number a is repeated on succeeding quotient polynomials until just a remainder is obtained, the remainders at each step of this process are

$$
P_n(a),\ P'_n(a),\ \frac{P''_n(a)}{2!},\ \frac{P'''_n(a)}{3!},\ \ldots,\ \frac{P_n^{(n)}(a)}{n!}.
$$

Demonstrate this on the polynomial $P_5(x) = x^5 + 4x^3 - 3x + 2$ with the number $a = 2$.

2.4 Method of False Position (Regula Falsi)

One of the best known methods of successive approximations to a real root of an equation is that known as the method of false position.

Suppose $f(x)$ is continuous between x_1 and x_2 and that $f(x_1)$ and $f(x_2)$ are of opposite sign. A third value, x_3, can be found, as the x intercept of the line segment joining the points $(x_1, f(x_1))$ and $(x_2, f(x_2))$. If there

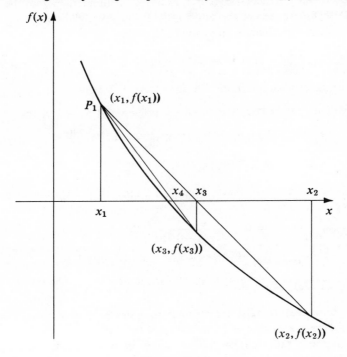

FIGURE 2.4.1

is but a single root α of $f(x) = 0$ between x_1 and x_2 then x_3 is closer to the root, α, than at least one of the values x_1 and x_2, since α and x_3 both lie in the interval (x_1, x_2) (Theorem 2.1.1).

The functional relationship between these three values of x can be seen by considering the geometrical representation of Figure 2.4.1. By similar triangles,

$$\frac{x_3 - x_1}{f(x_1)} = \frac{x_2 - x_1}{f(x_1) - f(x_2)} \tag{2.4.1}$$

or

$$x_3 = x_1 + \frac{f(x_1)}{f(x_1) - f(x_2)} (x_2 - x_1). \tag{2.4.2}$$

Equation 2.4.2 is then applied again with x_3 replacing either x_1 or x_2, whichever of these yields a value of $f(x)$ which is the same in sign as $f(x_3)$. If the values of x_1 and x_2 are sufficiently close so that only one root lies in the interval (x_1, x_2), successive applications of Equation 2.4.2 will give a sequence of values, x_i, such that $|x_i - x_{i-1}| \leq |x_{i-1} - x_{i-2}|$. The proof that the sequence so obtained converges to α is left as a problem for the student (see Problem 2.10).

EXAMPLE 2.4.1   Find a positive root of the equation

$$e^x - 3x = 0.$$

Solution: Since $f(x) = e^x - 3x$, and using 2.7183 to represent e,

$$f(0) = 1, f(1) = -0.2817.$$

Let $x_1 = 0$ and $x_2 = 1$. Then

$$x_3 = 0 + \frac{1}{1 - (-0.2817)} (1) = 0.780$$

and

$$f(x_3) = e^{0.78} - 3(0.78) = -0.1585.$$

Let $x_1 = 0$ and $x_2 = 0.780$ for the next application. Then

$$x_4 = 0 + \frac{1}{1 - (-0.1585)} (0.78) = 0.6633,$$

$$f(x_4) = e^{0.6633} - 3(0.6633) = -0.0488.$$

Let $x_2 = 0.6633$ replace $x_2 = 0.780$ for the next step. Then

$$x_5 = 0 + \frac{1}{1 - (-0.0488)} (0.6633) = 0.6324,$$

$$f(0.6324) = e^{0.6324} - 3(0.6324) = -0.0151.$$

Another iteration with $x_1 = 0$, $x_2 = 0.6324$ gives

$$x_6 = 0 + \frac{1}{1 - (-0.0151)} (0.6324) = 0.6230,$$

$$f(0.6320) = -0.0045.$$

Hence $x = 0.6320$ is a fairly good approximation to the desired root.

EXAMPLE 2.4.2   Use the method of false position to approximate the positive root of the equation $x^3 - 3 = 0$, through the second approximation.

Solution: Figure 2.2.1 indicates a root of this equation between $x = 1.4$ and 1.6. In Example 2.3.1, it is shown that the root actually lies between 1.4 and 1.5 and, incidentally, that there is no positive real root larger than 1.5. Using the method of false position with $x_1 = 1.4$ and $x_2 = 1.5$,

$$x_3 = 1.4 + \frac{-0.256}{-0.256 - 0.375}(0.1) \approx 1.44.$$

To find $f(1.44)$:

1	0	0	-3	$\lfloor 1.44$
	1.44	2.0736	2.985984	
1	1.44	2.0736	-0.014016	

Since $f(1.44) \approx -0.014$,

$$x_4 = 1.44 + \frac{-0.014}{-0.014 - 0.375}(0.06) \approx 1.442.$$

A computer program for using the method of false position requires, then, a routine for evaluation of Equation 2.4.2 for a given function $f(x)$, a routine to evaluate $f(x)$ for a particular x_i, and a routine for selecting the two points to retain.

Since $f(x_i)$ is to be calculated at each step, a test on the $f(x_i)$ can be added to this program and the process terminated when $f(x_i)$ is sufficiently close to zero; that is when $|f(x_i)| < \delta$, for some predetermined δ.

Exercise

1. Suppose that the false position method is used to approximate the root α of $f(x) = 0$. Suppose further that the iteration will be stopped when $|f(x_i)| < \epsilon$ for some preassigned $\epsilon > 0$.

If $f(x)$ satisfies the conditions for the Mean Value Theorem, show that

$$|x_i - \alpha| < \frac{\epsilon}{|f'(\delta)|} \text{ for } \delta \text{ a point between } x_i \text{ and } \alpha.$$

2.5 A Class of Iterative Methods

The general aim of iterative methods for finding a real root of an equation is to find a recursion formula by which a converging sequence of successive approximations may be computed, given an initial approximation sufficiently close to the desired root.

Let the equation

$$f(x) = 0 \tag{2.5.1}$$

be replaced by

$$x = g(x), \tag{2.5.2}$$

where $g(x)$ is to be defined such that all roots of Equation 2.5.1 are roots of Equation 2.5.2, and such that the recursion formula

$$x_{i+1} = g(x_i) \tag{2.5.3}$$

yields a sequence of values which converge to the desired root, α, under proper choice of x_0.

The equation, $f(x) = 0$, might be solved for x explicitly to determine $g(x)$ or the function, $g(x)$, might be defined as

$$g(x) = x - f(x). \tag{2.5.4}$$

In either of these cases, Equation 2.5.2 has precisely the roots of Equation 2.5.1. However, the sequence, $\{x_i\}$, defined by Equation 2.5.3, may not satisfy conditions for convergence (see Appendix E). An alternate definition for $g(x)$ might be

$$g(x) = x - h(x)g(x), \tag{2.5.5}$$

where $h(x)$ is finite at each root of $f(x)$.

In this case, every root of Equation 2.5.1 is a root of Equation 2.5.2, though not necessarily conversely. It is necessary, then, to determine the restrictions on $h(x)$ to assure that the sequence of Equation 2.5.3 converges to α. Consider an interval $(x, 2\alpha - x)$ which is an interval centered at α containing both the desired root, α, and the first approximation x_0.

If, for some k

$$\left| \frac{g(x_a) - g(x_b)}{x_a - x_b} \right| \le k \tag{2.5.6}$$

for every x_a and x_b in the given interval, then in particular

$$|g(x_i) - g(\alpha)| \le k |x_i - \alpha| \tag{2.5.7}$$

if x_i is in the given interval. But from Equation 2.5.2

$$g(\alpha) = \alpha. \tag{2.5.8}$$

Use of Equations 2.5.8 and 2.5.3 in Equation 2.5.7 gives

$$|x_{i+1} - \alpha| \le k |x_i - \alpha|. \tag{2.5.9}$$

Now if $k \le 1$, Equation 2.5.9 specifies that if x_i is in the given interval, x_{i+1} is in the interval also.

The interval $(x, 2\alpha - x)$ was defined to contain both x_0 and α; hence, by Equation 2.5.9,

$$|x_1 - \alpha| \le k |x_0 - \alpha|. \tag{2.5.10}$$

Then, since x_0 is in the interval, by Equation 2.5.9, x_1 is in the interval and

$$|x_2 - \alpha| \le k |x_1 - \alpha| \le k^2 |x_0 - \alpha| \tag{2.5.11}$$

and, by repeated application of Equation 2.5.9,

$$|x_{i+1} - \alpha| \le k^{i+1} |x_0 - \alpha|. \tag{2.5.12}$$

But, for $k < 1$, the right side of this last inequality may be made arbitrarily small for i sufficiently large and the sequence defined by Equation 2.5.3 thus converges to α.

It can be shown (see the problems at the end of this section) that if $g(x)$ has a continuous derivative in a closed interval containing α and if $|g'(\alpha)| < k < 1$, then there is an interval $(x, 2\alpha - x)$ for which the relation in Equation 2.5.6 is satisfied. Since $k < 1$ was the condition for convergence, then

$$\left. \begin{array}{l} g'(x) \text{ continuous in a closed interval} \\ \quad \text{containing } \alpha \\ \\ |g'(\alpha)| < k < 1 \end{array} \right\} \qquad (2.5.13)$$

and

constitute a sufficient condition for convergence of the sequence of Equation 2.5.3 for $g(x)$ as defined in Equation 2.5.4. Since the root, α, is not known, this condition is applied indirectly by determining an interval on the x-axis which contains α (by Theorem 2.1.1 for example) and in which $g'(x) < k < 1$.

The convergence of the sequence $\{x_i\}$ specified by Equation 2.5.3 is illustrated graphically in Figures 2.5.1, a, b, c, and d. In each of these figures the two functions

$$y = x, \qquad (2.5.14)$$
$$y = g(x) \qquad (2.5.15)$$

are plotted and the iterates $x_0, x_1, x_2, \ldots$ and $y_0, y_1, y_2, \ldots$ as found by the formulas

$$y_0 = g(x_0),$$
$$x_1 = y_0, \qquad y_1 = g(x_1), \qquad (2.5.16)$$
$$x_2 = y_1, \qquad y_2 = g(x_2).$$

are located on the graphs.

In Figure 2.5.4a, $g(x)$ has a positive slope less than 1 and the iterates $x_0, x_1, x_2 \ldots$ approach α along a stepped path.

In Figure 2.5.4b, $g(x)$ has a negative slope which is less than 1 in magnitude and the iterates $x_0, x_1, x_2, \ldots$ approach α by means of a rectangular spiral.

In Figures 2.5.4c and d, the slope of $g(x)$ is larger than 1 in magnitude and it is seen that the iterates $x_0, x_1, x_2, \ldots$ do not approach α, but diverge.

Under some circumstances a satisfactory test for deciding when to terminate an iteration is to test the size of $|x_{n+1} - x_n|$ at the $(n + 1)$st iteration, for $n = 0, 1, 2, \ldots$. If

$$x_{n+1} = \alpha + \epsilon_{n+1}$$

and

$$x_n = \alpha + \epsilon_n, \qquad (2.5.17)$$

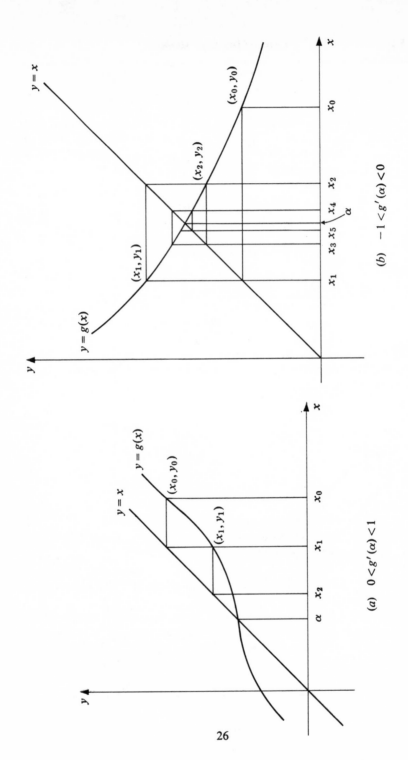

(a) $0 < g'(\alpha) < 1$

FIGURE 2.5.1a

(b) $-1 < g'(\alpha) < 0$

FIGURE 2.5.1b

26

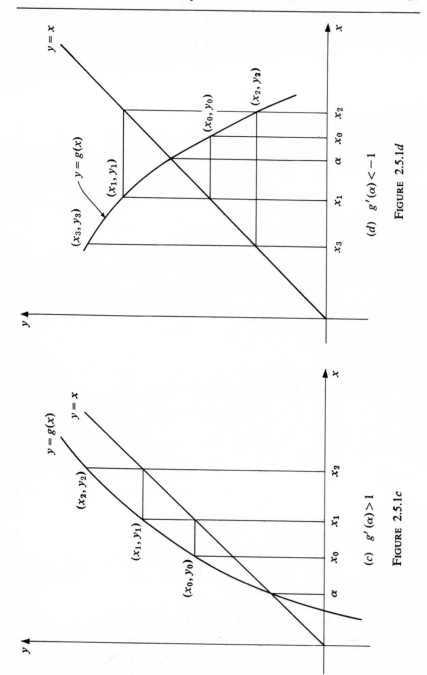

(d) $g'(\alpha) < -1$

FIGURE 2.5.1d

(c) $g'(\alpha) > 1$

FIGURE 2.5.1c

then
$$|x_{n+1} - x_n| = |\epsilon_{n+1} - \epsilon_n|. \tag{2.5.18}$$

Hence,
$$|\epsilon_n| - |\epsilon_{n+1}| \le |x_{n+1} - x_n| \le |\epsilon_n| + |\epsilon_{n+1}|. \tag{2.5.19}$$

From the inequality of Equation 2.5.7
$$|\epsilon_{n+1}| = |x_{n+1} - \alpha| = |g(x_n) - g(\alpha)| \le k\,|x_n - \alpha| = k\,|\epsilon_n|. \tag{2.5.20}$$

But then
$$|\epsilon_n| + |\epsilon_{n+1}| \le (1 + k)\,|\epsilon_n|,$$
$$|\epsilon_n| - |\epsilon_{n+1}| \ge (1 - k)\,|\epsilon_n|. \tag{2.5.21}$$

Substituting the inequalities in Equation 2.5.21 into the inequality in Equation 2.5.19 gives
$$(1 - k)\,|\epsilon_n| \le |x_{n+1} - x_n| \le (1 + k)\,|\epsilon_n|. \tag{2.5.22}$$

Hence, if k is close to 0, $|x_{n+1} - x_n|$ is close to $|\epsilon_n|$. In this case $|x_{n+1} - x_n|$ being small implies that the error in x_n is small, so that the error in x_{n+1} should be smaller still. However, when k is close to 1, the inequality of Equation 2.5.22 simply shows that $|x_{n+1} - x_n|$ is less than or equal to $2\,|\epsilon_n|$. Hence in this latter case the test is not adequate.

Exercises

1. Show that if $g'(x)$ is continuous in a closed interval centered at α and if $|g'(\alpha)| < k < 1$, then for every $\epsilon > 0$ there is a $\delta > 0$ such that
$$|g'(x)| < \epsilon + k$$
for
$$|x - \alpha| < \delta.$$

2. Use the definition of derivative to show that for any $\eta > 0$
$$|g(x_1) - g(x)| < (\eta + |g'(x)|)\,|x_1 - x|$$
for any x_1 and x sufficiently close to α.

3. Use the results of Exercises 1 and 2 to show that
$$|g(x_1) - g(x)| < K\,|x_1 - x|$$
for $K < 1$ and for all x_1 and x sufficiently close to α.

2.6 Order of Iteration Method

It is possible to define $h(x)$ in Equation 2.5.5 not only to assure convergence but to provide different rates of convergence. To this end, assuming the necessary conditions on $g(x)$, expand $g(x)$ in a neighborhood of α by means of a Taylor's expansion. Thus

$$g(x) = g(\alpha) + (x - \alpha)g'(\alpha) + \frac{(x - \alpha)^2}{2}g''(\alpha) + \cdots + \frac{(x - \alpha)^{n-1}}{(n - 1)!}g^{(n-1)}(\alpha)$$

$$+ \frac{(x - \alpha)^n}{n!}g^{(n)}(p) \qquad (p \text{ between } x \text{ and } \alpha). \qquad (2.6.1)$$

If x is replaced by x_i and use is made of Equations 2.5.8 and 2.5.3, Equation 2.6.1 can be written as

$$x_{i+1} - \alpha = (x_i - \alpha)g'(\alpha) + \frac{(x_i - \alpha)^2}{2}g''(\alpha) + \cdots + \frac{(x_i - \alpha)^{n-1}}{(n - 1)!}g^{(n-1)}(\alpha)$$

$$+ \frac{(x_i - \alpha)^n}{n!}g^{(n)}(p_i). \qquad (2.6.2)$$

Definition 2.6.1 If $g^{(m)}(\alpha) \neq 0$ and $g^{(j)}(\alpha) = 0$ for all $j < m$, the iteration method of Section 2.5 is said to be of *order m*.

For example, if $g'(\alpha) \neq 0$, Equation 2.6.2 may be written as

$$x_{i+1} - \alpha = (x_i - \alpha)g'(p_i) \qquad (p_i \text{ between } x_i \text{ and } \alpha) \qquad (2.6.3)$$

and the method is a *first order* method. If the sequence $\{x_i\}$ converges to α, then as $i \to \infty$, $p_i \to \alpha$ and $g'(p_i) \to g'(\alpha)$. Hence for i sufficiently large, successive iterations yield an error, $x_{i+1} - \alpha$, which is essentially a constant, $g'(\alpha)$, times the error in the preceding step.

On the other hand, for a second order method, with $g'(\alpha) = 0$, $g''(\alpha) \neq 0$, Equation 2.6.2 can be written as

$$x_{i+1} - \alpha = \frac{(x_i - \alpha)^2 g''(p_i)}{2} \qquad (p_i \text{ between } \alpha \text{ and } x_i) \qquad (2.6.4)$$

and the error in x_{i+1} is proportional to the square of the preceding error.

In a like manner, a higher order method, in which a higher order derivative, say the mth, is the first nonzero derivative at $x = \alpha$, can be seen to give successive errors which are proportional to the corresponding higher power, m, of the preceding error.

For $m \geq 2$, $g'(\alpha) = 0$. Hence by the conditions of Equation 2.5.13, any m-order method for $m \geq 2$ will converge to α if only x_0 is selected in the interval about α for which $|g'(x)| < 1$.

It can be shown that the method of false position can be considered to belong to the class of solutions under discussion and is, in fact, a first order method. (See Problem 2.9.)

2.7 A Second Order Method; Newton–Raphson Formula

In order to define $h(x)$ to assure a second order method, that is such that $g'(\alpha) = 0$, differentiate Equation 2.5.5 and evaluate the derivative at

$x = \alpha$. Thus

$$g'(x)\Big|_{x=\alpha} = 1 - h'(x)f(x) - h(x)f'(x)\Big|_{x=\alpha} \qquad (2.7.1)$$

or, since $f(\alpha) = 0$,

$$g'(\alpha) = 1 - h(\alpha)f'(\alpha). \qquad (2.7.2)$$

Then, for $g'(\alpha) = 0$

$$h(\alpha) = \frac{1}{f'(\alpha)}. \qquad (2.7.3)$$

If now $h(x)$ is defined as

$$h(x) = \frac{1}{f'(x)}, \qquad (2.7.4)$$

then Equation 2.7.3 is satisfied. With this choice of $h(x)$ Equation 2.5.5 is rewritten as

$$g(x) = x - \frac{f(x)}{f'(x)}. \qquad (2.7.5)$$

Equation 2.5.3 then becomes

$$x_{i+1} = x_i - \frac{f(x_i)}{f'(x_i)}. \qquad (2.7.6)$$

This is a second order formula called the *Newton–Raphson* formula.

Since the Newton-Raphson formula is, by definition, a second order method, the error at any step in the iteration is proportional to the square of the error at the preceding step, i.e.,

$$x_{i+1} - \alpha = (x_i - \alpha)^2 \frac{g''(p_i)}{2} \qquad (p_i \text{ between } x_i \text{ and } \alpha). \qquad (2.7.7)$$

Since some measure of the accuracy of the first approximation, x_0, is usually available, Equation 2.7.7 expressed in terms of x_0 would be more useful. By Equation 2.7.7

$$x_1 - \alpha = (x_0 - \alpha)^2 \frac{g''(p_1)}{2},$$

$$x_2 - \alpha = (x_1 - \alpha)^2 \frac{g''(p_2)}{2} = (x_0 - \alpha)^4 \left(\frac{g''(p_1)}{2}\right)^2 \frac{g''(p_2)}{2}, \qquad (2.7.8)$$

or, in general,

$$x_k - \alpha = (x_0 - \alpha)^{2^k} \left(\frac{g''(p_1)}{2}\right)^{2^{k-1}} \left(\frac{g''(p_2)}{2}\right)^{2^{k-2}} \cdots \frac{g''(p_k)}{2}, \qquad (2.7.9)$$

where the p_i are in the range between x_i and α. Since the sequence is converging, all x_i lie between x_0 and $2\alpha - x_0$, and $g''(x)$ is finite in this region. If, then, $g''(p)$ is the largest of the $g''(p_i)$ in the region, Equation

2.7.9 can be approximated by

$$|x_k - \alpha| \leq |(x_0 - \alpha)|^{2^k} \left| \left(\frac{g''(p)}{2} \right)^{(2^k - 1)} \right|. \tag{2.7.10}$$

EXAMPLE 2.7.1   Use the Newton–Raphson formula to find the real root of the equation $x^3 - 3 = 0$.

Solution: Since $f(x) = x^3 - 3$, then $f'(x) = 3x^2$ and Equation 2.7.6 becomes

$$x_{i+1} = x_i - \frac{x_i^3 - 3}{3x_i^2} = \frac{2x_i^3 - 3}{3x_i^2}.$$

In Example 2.3.1 it is shown that a real root of $x^3 - 3 = 0$ lies between $x = 1.4$ and $x = 1.5$. Let $x_0 = 1.4$. Then

$$x_1 = \frac{2(1.4)^3 + 3}{3(1.4)^2} = 1.4435,$$

$$x_2 = \frac{2(1.4435)^3 + 3}{3(1.4435)^2} = 1.44225.$$

Before forming more iterations, it is advisable to examine the error function. The error at any step is a function of $g''(x)$ and the preceding error. For this example,

$$g(x) = \frac{2x^3 + 3}{3x^2} = \frac{2x}{3} + \frac{1}{x^2}.$$

Then

$$g'(x) = \frac{2}{3} - \frac{2}{x^3}$$

and

$$g''(x) = \frac{6}{x^4}.$$

The initial error is less than 0.1, since the root is known to lie between $x = 1.4$ and $x = 1.5$. The value of $g''(x)$ for $x = 1.4$ is less than 2 and will decrease as x increases, that is as $x \to \alpha$. Since p_i in Equation 2.7.7 is always between x_i and α,

$$\left| \frac{g''(p_i)}{2} \right| < 1.$$

Then, at the first step

$$|x_i - \alpha| < (0.1)^2 = 0.01$$

and at the second step

$$|x_2 - \alpha| < (0.1)^4 = 0.0001$$

and the value given by x_2 varies from the true root by not more than 0.0001. The value given for this root, that is $\sqrt[3]{3}$, in a table is 1.442250.

EXAMPLE 2.7.2   Use the Newton–Raphson formula to find a positive root of $xe^x - 2 = 0$.

Solution: For this example,

$$f(x) = xe^x - 2,$$
$$f'(x) = e^x(x + 1),$$

and

$$g(x) = x - \frac{xe^x - 2}{e^x(x + 1)} = \frac{x^2 e^x + 2}{e^x(x + 1)}.$$

Since $f(0) = -2$, $f(0.5) = -1.1757$ and $f(1) = +0.7183$, there is a root for $0.5 < x < 1$. Let $x_0 = 0.8$. Then

$$x_1 = \frac{(0.8)^2 e^{0.8} + 2}{e^{0.8} 1.8} = 0.856$$

and

$$x_2 = \frac{(0.856)^2 e^{0.856} + 2}{e^{0.856} 1.856} = 0.8526.$$

The error analysis for this function is a little more difficult than that for Example 2.7.1 because the derivatives are less simple functions. However, with some perseverance the second derivative $g''(x)$ can be found to be

$$g''(x) = \frac{2[e^x + x^2 + 4x + 5]}{e^x(x + 1)^3} = \frac{2}{(x + 1)^3} + \frac{2(x^2 + 4x + 5)}{e^x(x + 1)^3}.$$

Since, in the interval (x_0, α), $x \geq 0.8$, inspection of $g''(x)$ shows that in this interval $g''(x_i) < 2$ and

$$|x_{i+1} - \alpha| \leq |(x_i - \alpha)^2| \left| \frac{g''(p_i)}{2} \right| \leq |(x_i - \alpha)^2|.$$

Hence, since $f(0.8) = -0.2196$ and $f(0.9) = 0.2136$, $x_0 = 0.8$ is in error by less than 0.1. The second iteration is then in error by less than $(0.1)^4$.

When the root α of $f(x) = 0$ is a double root, then both $f(x_i)$ and $f'(x_i)$ approach zero as x_i approaches α. The fraction $\dfrac{f(x_i)}{f'(x_i)}$ can then approach zero or increase without bound according as $f(x_i)$ approaches zero more or less rapidly than $f'(x_i)$. Hence, multiple roots present difficulties for the Newton–Raphson method. Indeed, when multiple roots are suspected, an alternative method of solution is probably needed.

While this chapter is concerned only with real roots, the methods discussed apply to complex roots as well. The conditions for convergence are altered slightly in this case. The location of the first approximation may be considerably more difficult for complex roots, since the graphical method is not applicable. However, the methods are not restricted to exclude complex roots.

The Newton–Raphson method is well adapted to use on an automatic computer. The program for this method can be essentially in three parts; a general program to evaluate Equation 2.7.6, given x_i and any $f(x)$, and two subroutines (or program parts) to evaluate $f(x_i)$ and $f'(x_i)$ for the particular problem.

If the Newton–Raphson method were to be programmed for an arbitrary equation $f(x) = 0$, several difficulties would occur. Among these are: (1) The first approximation must be so well chosen that convergence occurs and to the desired root. (2) Having found one root α, some way must be built into the program to start approximating the next root. (3) Some way of terminating the sequence $x_0, x_1, x_2, \ldots$, which is converging to a root α, must be incorporated in the program.

The last problem can usually be taken care of simply by testing the size of $|x_{n+1} - x_n|$ at each step in the process, as discussed in Section 2.5. The second problem can be handled simply be starting the process over with a new first approximation sufficiently close to the second root. Obviously, this brings up the first difficulty again. In the case when $f(x)$ is a polynomial, a second way of finding more than one root would be to divide $f(x)$ by $x - \alpha$, where α is the approximation to the first root. However, $\dfrac{f(x)}{x - \alpha}$ will be a polynomial whose coefficients are inaccurate due to α's being inaccurate and due to the pseudo-division used. Hence this method is not highly recommended.

The problem of selecting a first approximation is of course a difficult one. For polynomials of specific kinds, such as $x^n - N$, the first approximations can be readily determined. However, some ingenuity is usually required to find a suitable first approximation. For some not very encouraging words on this problem the reader should see *Mathematical Methods for Digital Computers* by Wilf and Ralston,[*] pp. 236–241.

Exercise

If the Newton–Raphson iteration formula converges for a given $f(x)$ and x_0, it actually converges to a root, α, of the equation $x = g(x)$. Show that the root α also satisfies $f(x) = 0$.

2.8   Formulas for Roots and Reciprocals by the Newton–Raphson Formula

For an integral root of a number N, let

$$f(x) = x^n - N. \tag{2.8.1}$$

[*] H. S. Wilf, and Anthony Ralston, *Mathematical Methods for Digital Computers*, John Wiley and Sons, Inc., New York, 1960.

Then

$$f'(x) = nx^{n-1},$$ (2.8.2)

and the Newton–Raphson iteration formula is

$$x_{i+1} = x_i - \frac{x_i^n - N}{nx_i^{n-1}} = \frac{(n-1)x_i^n + N}{nx_i^{n-1}}.$$ (2.8.3)

In particular, for $n = 3$

$$x_{i+1} = \frac{2x_i + N}{3x_i^2}.$$ (2.8.4)

This is just the formula used in Example 2.7.1. If $n = 2$, the formula for the square root is

$$x_{i+1} = \frac{x_i^2 + N}{2x_i}.$$ (2.8.5)

The problem of determining a first approximation which is inside the interval in which convergence is guaranteed is usually difficult. However, in the case of the Newton–Raphson square root formula a complete answer to the selection of the first approximation can be given. From Equation 2.8.5

$$g(x) = \frac{x^2 + N}{2x}.$$ (2.8.6)

The first approximation x_0 must be chosen in an interval centered at α for which for some $k < 1$

$$|g(x_1) - g(x_2)| \le k\,|x_1 - x_2|$$ (2.8.7)

for all x_1 and x_2 in the interval. But from Equation 2.8.6,

$$|g(x_1) - g(x_2)| = \left| \frac{x_1^2 + N}{2x_1} - \frac{x_2^2 + N}{2x_2} \right|$$

$$= \frac{1}{2}\left| 1 - \frac{N}{x_1 x_2} \right| |x_1 - x_2|.$$ (2.8.8)

Now

$$\frac{1}{2}\left| 1 - \frac{N}{x_1 x_2} \right| < 1$$

implies that

$$-2 < 1 - \frac{N}{x_1 x_2} < 2$$ (2.8.9)

or

$$x_1 x_2 > \frac{N}{3}.$$ (2.8.10)

Hence, x_0 must be chosen so that $x_0{}^2 > (N/3)$. Now if x_0 is to be in an interval centered at $\sqrt{N}$ with the left end point being $\sqrt{N/3}$, then the interval $(\sqrt{N/3}, 2\sqrt{N} - \sqrt{N/3})$ is safe. However, the upper end point is difficult to use. But since $\sqrt{N/3} < \sqrt{N}$, hence $0 < \sqrt{N} - \sqrt{N/3}$ or $\sqrt{N} < 2\sqrt{N} - \sqrt{N/3}$. Therefore a choice of x_0 such that $(N/3) < x_0{}^2 < N$ does place x_0 in an interval centered at $\sqrt{N}$ for which the Lipschitz condition applies. Hence, if $x_0{}^2$ is between $N/3$ and N, the iteration will converge.

EXAMPLE 2.8.1   Find the positive square root of 2 by using the Newton-Raphson formula.

Solution: For this problem $f(x) = x^2 - 2$. By synthetic division, the root may be located to one decimal place.

1	0	-2	$\lfloor 1$
	1	1	
1	1	-1	

1	0	-2	$\lfloor 2$
	2	4	
1	2	2	

1	0	-2	$\lfloor 1.5$
	1.5	2.25	
1	1.5	0.25	

1	0	-2	$\lfloor 1.4$
	1.4	1.96	
1	1.4	-0.04	

Hence a root lies between $x = 1.4$ and $x = 1.5$.

Since $x_0 = 1.4$ satisfies the condition of the inequality in Equation 2.8.8, let $x_0 = 1.4$; then $|x_0 - \alpha| < 0.1$ and

$$x_1 = \frac{(1.4)^2 + 2}{2.8} = 1.4143,$$

$$x_2 = \frac{(1.4143)^2 + 2}{2.8286} = 1.41421.$$

From Equation 2.8.5, with $N = 2$

$$g(x) = \frac{x^2 + 2}{2x}.$$

Then, for $x = 1.4$

$$g''(x) = \frac{2}{x^3} = \frac{2}{(1.4)^3}$$

and $g''(x) < 1$ and decreases as x increases. Since $|x_0 - \alpha| < 0.1$, then $|x_2 - \alpha| < (0.1)^4 \dfrac{g''(p)^3}{2}$, by using Equation 2.7.10 for p between $x = 1.4$

and $x = 2\alpha - 1.4$. Since $\alpha > 1.4$, then $x = 1.4$ is the left end point of the interval, and p must then satisfy $p > 1.4$. Hence $g''(p) < 1$ and

$$|x_2 - \alpha| < \frac{(0.1)^4}{2}.$$

One more synthetic division reveals that, in fact,

$$|x_0 - \alpha| < 0.02 \text{ and } |x_2 - \alpha| < (0.02)^4 = 16 \times 10^{-8}.$$

For the reciprocal of a number, N, let

$$f(x) = \frac{1}{x} - N \qquad (2.8.11)$$

and

$$f'(x) = -\frac{1}{x^2}. \qquad (2.8.12)$$

Hence, the Newton–Raphson iteration formula for the reciprocal of N is

$$x_{i+1} = x_i - \frac{\dfrac{1}{x_i} - N}{\dfrac{1}{x_i^2}} = x_i(2 - Nx_i). \qquad (2.8.13)$$

EXAMPLE 2.8.2   Use Equation 2.8.13 to find the reciprocal of 2.15.

Solution: Let $x_0 = 0.5$,

$$x_1 = 0.5(2 - 0.5 \times 2.15) = 0.4625,$$
$$x_2 = 0.4625[2 - (2.15)(0.4625)] = 0.465101,$$
$$x_3 = 0.465102[2 - (2.15)(0.465102)] = 0.46511628.$$

From Equation 2.8.13

$$g(x) = x(2 - Nx)$$

and

$$g''(x) = -2N.$$

Since, for this example, $f(0.5) = -0.15$ and $f(0.4) = +0.35$, then $|x_0 - \alpha| < 0.1$ and by Equation 2.7.10

$$|x_3 - \alpha| < (0.1)^8 N^7 = (0.1)^8 x(2.15)^7 \approx 212.3 \times 10^{-8}.$$

Comparison of the result given by x_3 and the value of 0.4651162791, as determined by division, shows the error is actually on the order of 1×10^{-9}.

2.9 Finding All Real Roots of a Polynomial Equation

In general, finding each root of an equation is a separate problem in which the approximate root is first found and one of the iteration methods used to find a satisfactorily close approximation to the root.

In the case in which $f(x) = P_n(x)$, however, it is possible to reduce the degree of the polynomial by one for each root located by use of Property 2.3.1. By this property, if $x = a$ is a root of $P_n(x) = 0$, then $P_n(x)$ can be expressed as

$$P_n(x) = (x - a)P_{n-1}(x), \qquad (2.9.1)$$

where $P_{n-1}(x)$ is the quotient in the division of $P_n(x)$ by $x - a$. Using synthetic division, the first n terms resulting from the synthetic division of a polynomial by a number, a, are the coefficients of the new polynomial of degree $n - 1$, when the last term, or remainder, is zero. This new polynomial may now be treated as a new problem and a root isolated and divided out.

The virtue of this method is that the expressions for $f(x)$ and $g(x)$ are simplified at each step. The last two roots can also be found by use of the quadratic formula when the quotient polynomial reaches degree 2, as it always will if both real and complex roots are found or if the polynomial has not more than two complex roots.

The disadvantage of using reduced polynomials over that of using the original polynomial in every case is the fact that in reducing the polynomial $P_n(x)$ by division by $x - \alpha$, errors in the coefficients of the reduced polynomial are introduced. Thus, for example, if $P_{n-1}(x) = 0$ should be $x^{39} = 0$, but due to a division error becomes instead $x^{39} - 10^{-39} = 0$ then an error of 10^{-39} in a coefficient has caused an error of 0.1 in a root. Although this is a bizarre case, it indicates how small errors in the coefficients of a polynomial may affect the roots. As a result, the process of successive reductions of degree is usually not too accurate.

EXAMPLE 2.9.1   Find all the roots of the polynomial

$$x^3 - 4x^2 - x + 24 = 0.$$

Solution: Inspection of synthetic division reveals the fact that a root lies between $x = 1$ and $x = 2$. This root can be shown to lie between $x = 1.8$ and $x = 1.9$ by synthetic division. The Newton–Raphson method requires $f'(x)$, which is

$$f'(x) = 3x^2 - 8x - 9.$$

Synthetic division is probably the simplest way to evaluate $f(x_i)$ and $f'(x_i)$.

Thus, if $x_0 = 1.8$, the following results are obtained.

$$
\begin{array}{rrrr}
1 & -4 & -9 & 24 \qquad \underline{|.8} \\
  & 1.8 & -3.96 & -23.328 \\
\hline
1 & -2.2 & -12.96 & 0.672 = f(x_0) \\
  & 1.8 & -0.72 \\
\hline
1 & -0.4 & -13.68 = f'(x_0)
\end{array}
$$

$$x_1 = 1.8 - \frac{0.672}{-13.68} = 1.849$$

$$
\begin{array}{rrrr}
1 & -4 & -9 & 24 \qquad \underline{|1.849} \\
  & 1.849 & -3.9772 & -23.99484 \\
\hline
1 & -2.151 & -12.9772 & 0.00516 = f(x_1) \\
  & 1.849 & -0.5584 \\
\hline
1 & -0.302 & -13.5356 = f'(x_1)
\end{array}
$$

$$x_2 = 1.849 - \frac{0.00516}{-13.5356} = 1.8494$$

$$
\begin{array}{rrrr}
1 & -4 & -9 & 24 \qquad \underline{|1.8494} \\
  & 1.8494 & -3.97732 & -24.000255 \\
\hline
1 & -2.1506 & -12.97732 & -0.000255 = f(x_2)
\end{array}
$$

Since $|x_0 - \alpha| < 0.1$, $|x_2 - \alpha| < (0.1)^4$, so $x = 1.8494$ is sufficiently close to the desired root. The remainder in the last division is another indication of the accuracy of the root.

The reduced polynomial is

$$x^2 - 2.1506 - 12.97732 = 0,$$

and by the quadratic formula the remaining two roots are found to be

$$x = -2.6841 \quad \text{and} \quad x = 4.8347.$$

It is interesting so see how closely these roots check in the original equation. This can be done by synthetic division thus.

$$
\begin{array}{rrrr}
1 & -4 & -9 & 24 \qquad \underline{|-2.6841} \\
  & -2.6841 & 17.9408 & -23.998 \\
\hline
1 & -6.6841 & 8.9408 & 0.002
\end{array}
$$

$$
\begin{array}{rrrr}
1 & -4 & -9 & 24 \qquad \underline{|4.8347} \\
  & 4.8347 & 4.0355 & -24.0019 \\
\hline
1 & 0.8347 & -4.9645 & -0.0019
\end{array}
$$

Problems

2.1 Use Theorem 2.1.1 to locate, in an interval with width of 0.1, a root of the following equations in the first cycle on the cosine curve.

(a) $e^x \cos \pi x = 0$

(b) $x - 2 \cos \dfrac{\pi}{12} x = 0$

2.2 Use synthetic division and Theorem 2.1.1 to locate, in a 0.1 interval, one real root of each of the following polynomials.

(a) $x^3 - 2x - 1 = 0$
(b) $x^4 + x^3 + x^2 + x - 1 = 0$
(c) $x^2 - 6 = 0$

2.3 Use Property 2.3.3 to find upper and lower bounds on the roots in Problem 2.2.

2.4 Show that $x = -1$ is an upper bound on the roots of

$$x^3 + 6x^2 + 11x + 6 = 0.$$

2.5 Solve Problem 2.1 by the graphical method.

2.6 Solve Problem 2.2 by the graphical method.

2.7 Show, by symbolic synthetic division of the polynomial

$$P_3(x) = a_3 x^3 + a_2 x^2 + a_1 x + a_0$$

by b, that the remainder term is indeed $P_3(b)$.

2.8 Use the method of false position to find the values of the roots located in Problem 2.1 to an accuracy sufficient to give four decimal places of accuracy in $f(x_i)$, i.e., $|f(x_i)| \leq 0.5 \times 10^{-4}$.

2.9 Use the method of false position to find the values of the roots located in Problem 2.2 to an accuracy sufficient to give three decimal places of accuracy in $f(x_i)$.

2.10 The method of "false position" can be put into the form of Equation 2.5.5 if $g(x)$ is defined by

$$g(x) = \frac{x_0 f(x) - x f(x_0)}{f(x) - f(x_0)}.$$

Under what conditions on $f(x)$ will the sequence $\{x_i\}$, where $x_i = g(x_{i-1})$, be a first order convergent sequence; i.e. $g'(\alpha) \neq 0$, $g'(\alpha) < 1$, and $g'(x)$ satisfies the conditions of Equation 2.5.13 ?

(Hint: use $g'(\alpha)$ and Taylor's expansion of $f(x_0)$ about α or use $g(\alpha)$ and a geometric analysis.)

2.11 Derive a formula for a third order iteration method.

2.12 Use the Newton–Raphson formula to find the values of the roots located in Problem 2.1 to four decimal place accuracy. Give details of your error analysis.

2.13 Repeat Problem 2.12 for the roots of the equations in Problem 2.2.

2.14 Use the Newton–Raphson formula to find the square root, cube root and reciprocal of each of the following numbers to four decimal places of accuracy. Give complete details of the error analysis in each case.

(a) 28.64, (b) 0.0378, (c) 6.15, (d) 0.876.

2.15 Find all the roots of the equation $x^4 - 5x^3 - 2x^2 + 9x - 12 = 0$, using the Newton–Raphson method to find the first root.

CHAPTER 3

Polynomial Approximations
and Finite Differences

MANY PROBLEMS ARISE in which it is desirable to represent a function by a second function which approximates the original one in some specified sense. One situation in which such a representing function is desirable is that in which the original function is known but either it or its derivative or integral may not be easily evaluated. For example, the function e^x is simple mathematically, but for numerical evaluation it must be represented by some approximating function.

A second situation in which an approximating function is needed is that in which only a limited number of functional values are known and not the function itself. Finally, most functions which are to be used in a digital computer must be approximated by a finite number of additions, subtractions, multiplications and divisions.

An approximating function may either coincide with a function at a certain number of points or it may simply approximate a certain number of points according to some specified criteria. It is the first of these two situations which is the subject of this chapter.

3.1 Finite Differences

An approximating function may be expressed in terms of given values of the original function directly. For example, in linear interpolation use is made of two values (ordinates) corresponding to two successive abscissas. For more accurate representation, more of the original information must be used. One of the ways in which this extra information is exploited requires the use of *finite differences*.

In general, it is not necessary that the spacing on the abscissas be equal but such equal spacing somewhat simplifies the problem and will, therefore, be used in this chapter. Concern will be with what is sometimes specified as descending differences but which will be called, simply, differences.

The first difference of a function, $y = f(x)$, for $x = x_i$ is referred to as $\Delta f(x_i) = \Delta y_i$ and is defined as

$$\Delta f(x_i) = \Delta y_i = f(x_{i+1}) - f(x_i), \qquad (3.1.1)$$

where

$$x_{i+1} = x_i + h \qquad (3.1.2)$$

and h is the uniform increment on x. The second difference is defined as $\Delta^2 y_i = \Delta(\Delta y_i)$, which from Equation 3.1.1 is

$$\Delta^2 y_i = \Delta(\Delta y_i) = \Delta y_{i+1} - \Delta y_i, \qquad (3.1.3)$$

and, in general, the nth difference is defined as $\Delta^n y_i = \Delta(\Delta^{n-1} y_i)$; hence

$$\Delta^n y_i = \Delta(\Delta^{n-1} y_i) = \Delta^{n-1} y_{i+1} - \Delta^{n-1} y_i \qquad (n \geq 2). \qquad (3.1.4)$$

Tables 3.1.1, 3.1.2 and 3.1.3 are suggested as the best arrangements for calculation of differences. These tables also show the relationships among the differences perhaps better than is possible by formal definitions.

Table 3.1.1

x	$f(x)$	$\Delta f(x)$	$\Delta^2 f(x)$	$\Delta^3 f(x)$
x_0	y_0			
		Δy_0		
x_1	y_1		$\Delta^2 y_0$	
		Δy_1		$\Delta^3 y_0$
x_2	y_2		$\Delta^2 y_1$	
		Δy_2		
x_3	y_3			

Table 3.1.2

x	$f(x)$	$\Delta f(x)$	$\Delta^2 f(x)$	$\Delta^3 f(x)$
x_0	y_0			
		$y_1 - y_0$		
x_1	y_1		$\Delta y_1 - \Delta y_0$	
		$y_2 - y_1$		$\Delta^2 y_1 - \Delta^2 y_0$
x_2	y_2		$\Delta y_2 - \Delta y_1$	
		$y_3 - y_2$		
x_3	y_3			

Differences may also be expressed in terms of functional values, as illustrated in the following table.

TABLE 3.1.3

x	$f(x)$	$\Delta f(x)$	$\Delta^2 f(x)$	$\Delta^3 f(x)$
x_0	y_0			
		$y_1 - y_0$		
x_1	y_1		$y_2 - 2y_1 + y_0$	
		$y_2 - y_1$		$y_3 - 3y_2 + 3y_1 - y_0$
x_2	y_2		$y_3 - 2y_2 + y_1$	
		$y_3 - y_2$		
x_3	y_3			

EXAMPLE 3.1.1

x	$y = f(x)$	Δy	$\Delta^2 y$	$\Delta^3 y$
0	1			
		0.0101		
0.01	1.0101		0	
		0.0101		0.0002
0.02	1.0202		0.0002	
		0.0103		
0.03	1.0305			

EXAMPLE 3.1.2

x	y	Δy	$\Delta^2 y$	$\Delta^3 y$	$\Delta^4 y$
1.0	0.1924				
		0.1009			
1.1	0.2933		0.0161		
		0.1170		0.0132	
1.2	0.4103		0.0293		0.0179
		0.1463		0.0311	
1.3	0.5566		0.0604		
		0.2067			
1.4	0.7633				

EXAMPLE 3.1.3 Find the first difference of the functions x, x^2, x^3 at $x = 2$, with $h = 2$.

Solution
$$\Delta x = x + h - x = h,$$
$$\Delta x^2 = (x + h)^2 - x^2 = 2xh + h^2,$$
$$\Delta x^3 = (x + h)^3 - x^3 = 3x^2h + 3xh^2 + h^3.$$

Hence
$$\Delta x \big|_{x=2} = 2,$$
$$\Delta x^2 \big|_{x=2} = 12,$$
$$\Delta x^3 \big|_{x=2} = 56.$$

Exercises

1. From Equations 3.1.1 and 3.1.2, it follows that $\Delta f(x)$ can be defined by $\Delta f(x) = f(x + h) - f(x)$. If $h = 1$, show that $\Delta 2^x = 2^x$.

2. The binomial coefficients are often written as $\binom{n}{m}$, that is, $\binom{n}{m} = \dfrac{n!}{(n-m)!\,m!}$. Show by induction that

$$\Delta^n y_0 = y_n - \binom{n}{1}y_{n-1} + \binom{n}{2}y_{n-2} + \cdots$$

$$+ (-1)^r \binom{n}{r} y_{n-r} + \cdots + (-1)^n y_0.$$

3. Prove that $\Delta C = 0$ for C a constant.

4. Use Exercises 2 and 3 to prove that

$$1 - \binom{n}{1} + \binom{n}{2} - \binom{n}{3} + \cdots + (-1)^n \cdot 1 = 0.$$

3.2 Factorial Polynomials

Since polynomials play a central role in the approximations discussed in this chapter, and since differences of powers of x are not simply expressed (see Examples 3.1.3), it is convenient to transform x to

$$u = \frac{x - x_0}{h}, \tag{3.2.1}$$

where x_0 and h are pre-assigned constants.

The variable u is then a function of x, say $u(x)$. One of the important properties of $u(x)$ is that

$$u(x + h) = \frac{x + h - x_0}{h} = \frac{x - x_0}{h} + 1 = u(x) + 1 \tag{3.2.2}$$

or in general
$$u(x + nh) = u(x) + n. \tag{3.2.3}$$

The concept of factorial polynomials is introduced to produce an analogue of powers of x and these factorials are defined as

$$u^{[0]} = 1,$$
$$u^{[1]} = u,$$
$$u^{[2]} = u(u - 1),$$
$$u^{[3]} = u(u - 1)(u - 2),$$

$$\cdot$$
$$\cdot \qquad\qquad\qquad\qquad\qquad (3.2.4)$$
$$\cdot$$

$$u^{[n]} = u(u - 1)(u - 2) \cdots (u - n + 1).$$

The difference for a factorial polynomial is given as

$$\Delta u^{[k]} = k u^{[k-1]}. \qquad\qquad (3.2.5)$$

Equation 3.2.5 can be proved by

$$\Delta u^{[k]} = u(x + h)^{[k]} - u(x)^{[k]} = (u + 1)^{[k]} - u^{[k]}, \qquad (3.2.6)$$

which in expanded form is

$$\Delta u^{[k]} = [(u + 1)(u)(u - 1) \cdots (u - k + 2)]$$
$$- [u(u - 1) \cdots (u - k + 1)]$$
$$= [u(u - 1) \cdots (u - k + 2)][(u + 1) - (u - k + 1)]$$
$$= k u^{[k-1]}.$$

(See Problems 3.3, 3.4, 3.5 and 3.6 for other relations involving factorial polynomials.)

Exercises

1. Show that

$$u^{[n]} = \frac{1}{h^n} (x - x_0)(x - x_1) \cdots (x - x_{n-1}).$$

2. Find $\Delta f(x)$ where $f(x) = a_0 x^3 + a_1 x^2 + a_2 x + a_3$.

3.3 A Polynomial as a Function of Differences

Any polynomial,

$$P_n(x) = a_n x^n + a_{n-1} x^{n-1} + \cdots + a_1 x + a_0, \qquad (3.3.1)$$

which is of degree n in x can be written in the form

$$P_n(x) = b_n u^{[n]} + b_{n-1} u^{[n-1]} + \cdots + b_1 u + b_0 \qquad (3.3.2)$$

for the proper values of the coefficients b_i. To determine the b_i coefficients, first compute successive differences on the terms of Equations 3.3.2, using the property that $\Delta(f + g) = \Delta f + \Delta g$. (See Problem 3.1.4.) Thus

$$\Delta P_n(x) = b_n n u^{[n-1]} + b_{n-1}(n - 1)u^{[n-2]} + \cdots + 2b_2 u^{[1]} + b_1,$$

$$\Delta^2 P_n(x) = n(n - 1)b_n u^{[n-2]} + (n - 1)(n - 2)b_{n-1}u^{[n-3]} + \cdots + 2b_2,$$

$$\vdots$$

$$\Delta^n P_n(x) = n!\, b_n. \tag{3.3.3}$$

If, now, $x = x_0$, then $u = \dfrac{x - x_0}{h} = 0$, and substitution of $x = x_0$ into Equations 3.3.2 and 3.3.3 gives

$$
\begin{aligned}
b_0 &= P_n(x_0), \\
b_1 &= \Delta P_n(x_0), \\
b_2 &= \frac{\Delta^2 P_n(x_0)}{2!}, \\
b_3 &= \frac{\Delta^3 P_n(x_0)}{3!}, \\
&\;\vdots \\
b_n &= \frac{\Delta^n P_n(x_0)}{n!}.
\end{aligned}
\tag{3.3.4}
$$

The coefficients in Equation 3.3.4 may seem a bit formidable on first glance but closer examination reveals that the $\Delta^k P_n(x_0)$ are just the differences, $\Delta^k y_0$, of the difference table in Table 3.1.1 if $y = P_n(x)$.

Equation 3.3.2 may now be written as

$$P_n(x) = \frac{\Delta^n P_n(x_0)}{n!} u^{[n]} + \frac{\Delta^{n-1} P_n(x_0)}{(n - 1)!} u^{[n-1]} + \cdots + \frac{\Delta P_n(x_0)}{1!} u + P_n(x_0)$$

$$\tag{3.3.5}$$

or

$$P_n(x) = \frac{\Delta^n y_0}{n!} u^{[n]} + \frac{\Delta^{n-1} y_0}{(n - 1)!} u^{[n-1]} + \cdots + \Delta y_0 u + y_0. \tag{3.3.6}$$

Probably the most important point to remark about the polynomial in Equation 3.3.5 or 3.3.6 is the fact that this polynomial *passes through* the points (x_i, y_i) in the difference table from which the coefficients are computed. That is, $P_n(x_i) = y_i$ for $i = 0, 1, 2, \ldots, n$.

To illustrate this, let $x_i = x_1$. Then, since $\Delta y_0 = y_1 - y_0$, $u_1 = u(x_1) = x_1 - x_0/h = 1$ and $u_1^{[k]} = 0$ for $k \geq 2$. Then

$$P_n(x_1) = y_0 + (y_1 - y_0) = y_1.$$

When $i = 2$, since $\Delta^2 y_0 = y_2 - 2y_1 + y_0$ and $u_2 = u(x_2) = \dfrac{x_2 - x_0}{h} = 2$, then $u_2^{[2]} = 2 \cdot 1$ and $u_2^{[k]} = 0$ for $k \geq 3$. Then

$$P_n(x_2) = y_0 + (y_1 - y_0)(2) + \frac{(y_2 - 2y_1 + y_0)(2)(1)}{2} + 0 = y_2.$$

In a like manner it can be shown that

$$P_n(x_i) = y_i, i = 0, 1, 2, \ldots, n.$$

In fact, a general proof is possible and is given in Appendix G.

The differences $\Delta y_0, \Delta^2 y_0, \ldots, \Delta^n y_0$ are called *leading differences* and it is easy to show that these n leading differences and the $n + 1$ points completely determine the whole difference table.

EXAMPLE 3.3.1   Express the polynomial

$$P_3(x) = 3x^3 - 4x^2 - 5x + 2$$

in terms of factorial polynomials, i.e., in the form of Equation 3.3.2.

Solution: Construct a difference table for $P_3(x)$ with $x_0 = 0$ and $h = 1$.

x	y	Δy	$\Delta^2 y$	$\Delta^3 y$
0	2			
		-6		
1	-4		10	
		4		18
2	0		28	
		32		
3	32			

Then

$$P_3(x) = \frac{18}{3!} u^{[3]} + \frac{10}{2!} u^{[2]} - 6u^{[1]} + 2$$

$$= 3u^{[3]} + 5u^{[2]} - 6u^{[1]} + 2.$$

It is shown in Section 3.4 that $n + 1$ points, $(x_0, y_0), (x_1, y_1), \ldots, (x_n, y_n)$, where all the x_i are distinct, uniquely determines a polynomial, $P_n(x)$, of degree at most n. Using this fact, it can be seen that *any* four points on the curve $y = P_3(x)$ could have been used in the example and yet produce exactly the same factorial polynomial in x. Since, however, $u = \dfrac{x - x_0}{h}$, if x_0 and h are changed, the polynomial in terms of u would *look* different. Expansion of both polynomials in terms of x, however, would give the same polynomial in x.

An interesting characteristic of difference tables for polynomials is revealed by an extension of the table of differences in Example 3.3.1 for more than four points.

x	y	Δy	$\Delta^2 y$	$\Delta^3 y$	$\Delta^4 y$
0	2				
		−6			
1	−4		10		
		4		18	
2	0		28		0
		32		18	
3	32		46		0
		78		18	
4	110		64		
		142			
5	252				

This illustrates the fact that for points computed from an mth degree polynomial, mth differences are all equal and hence all differences greater than the mth are zero.

Exercise

Find the equation of a polynomial curve which passes through the points $(-1, 2)$, $(0, 3)$, $(1, 4)$, $(2, 3)$.

3.4 Approximating Polynomial in Terms of Differences; Gregory–Newton Formula

The problem of concern in this chapter was defined as that of obtaining a function $g(x)$ which approximates a given function, $f(x)$, in that $g(x)$ agrees exactly with $f(x)$ at a certain number of specified points. One of the requirements for the new function $g(x)$ is simplicity of evaluation and a polynomial will certainly fit this requirement. A further property of polynomials adds greater weight to the selection of a polynomial as the new or approximating function. This property may be stated as follows.

Property 3.4.1 Given any $n + 1$ distinct number pairs (points), there exists a unique polynomial equation, $y = P_n(x)$, of degree n or less, which is satisfied by these $n + 1$ number pairs (or a polynomial curve which passes through the $n + 1$ points).

Proof: If

$$P_n(x) = a_0 + a_1 x + \cdots + a_n x^n, \tag{3.4.1}$$

then the coefficients are determined as the solution to the set of equations

$$a_0 + a_1 x_0 + \cdots + a_n x_0{}^n = P_n(x_0),$$
$$a_0 + a_1 x_1 + \cdots + a_n x_1{}^n = P_n(x_1),$$
$$\vdots \tag{3.4.2}$$
$$a_0 + a_1 x_n + \cdots + a_n x_n{}^n = P_n(x_n).$$

This system of equations has a unique solution for $a_0, a_1, \ldots, a_n$ if and only if the matrix of coefficients is nonsingular, that is if

$$\mathcal{A} = \begin{bmatrix} 1 & x_0 & x_0{}^2 & x_0{}^3 & \cdots & x_0{}^n \\ 1 & x_1 & x_1{}^2 & x_1{}^3 & \cdots & x_1{}^n \\ \vdots & & & & & \vdots \\ 1 & x_n & x_n{}^2 & x_n{}^3 & \cdots & x_n{}^n \end{bmatrix} \tag{3.4.3}$$

is nonsingular. The determinant of this matrix is the well-known Vandermonde determinant which is equal to

$$\prod_{\substack{i,j=0 \\ i>j}}^{n} (x_i - x_j) = (x_n - x_{n-1})(x_n - x_{n-2}) \cdots (x_n - x_0)(x_{n-1} - x_{n-2}) \cdots$$
$$(x_2 - x_1)(x_2 - x_0)(x_1 - x_0). \tag{3.4.4}$$

But for no two of the x_i equal, this product is not zero. Hence, for unique x_i, the matrix is nonsingular and there is one and only one set of coefficients for $P_n(x)$.

In the preceding section, Equation 3.3.6 is a formula for a polynomial which passes through a given set of points. Examination of this equation shows that for an nth degree polynomial the nth difference is the largest difference required. In addition, examination of a difference table reveals that to form an nth difference, the table must contain $n + 1$ points. This all suggests that Equation 3.3.6 is the polynomial through a set of $n + 1$ points with leading differences $\Delta y_0, \Delta^2 y_0, \ldots, \Delta^n y_0$. Such is indeed the case. Equation 3.3.6 is called the Gregory–Newton formula and is perhaps more usefully written as

$$y = y_0 + u^{[1]} \Delta y_0 + u^{[2]} \frac{\Delta^2 y_0}{2!} + u^{[3]} \frac{\Delta^3 y_0}{3!} + \cdots + u^{[n]} \frac{\Delta^3 y_0}{n!}. \tag{3.4.5}$$

While Equation 3.4.5 is very often called the Gregory–Newton formula for interpolation, it is first of all the equation of the polynomial curve, of degree n or less, which passes through a given set of $n + 1$ points. It can also be used, however, to find values of the function, $y = P_n(x)$, for any values of x in the interval (x_0, x_n), i.e., for interpolation, or even for extrapolation, i.e., finding the value of the function for a value of x outside the interval (x_0, x_n). The accuracy of both interpolation and extrapolation is discussed in a following section.

EXAMPLE 3.4.1   Given the difference table

x	y	Δy	$\Delta^2 y$	$\Delta^3 y$
0	-3			
		5		
0.1	2		0	
		5		-6
0.2	7		-6	
		-1		
0.3	6			

find the Gregory–Newton polynomial which passes through these points and use this polynomial to approximate the values of the function y at $x = 0.15$ and $x = 0.4$.

Solution: Substitution into Equation 3.4.5 from the table gives

$$P_3(x) = y = -3 + 5u^{[1]} - u^{[3]}.$$

When $x = 0.15$, since $h = 0.1$ and $x_0 = 0$, $u = 1.5$.   Then

$$P_3(0.15) = -3 + 5(1.5) - (1.5)(0.5)(-0.5) = 4.875.$$

When $x = 0.4$, then $u = \dfrac{0.4}{0.1} = 4$ and

$$P_3(0.4) = -3 + 5(4) - (4)(3)(2) = -7.$$

Formation of a finite difference table by means of a digital computer is not essentially difficult. The actual programming may be somewhat "tricky" in that changing counters will be involved since each column is computed by one less step than the previous column.

Once the table is constructed, the polynomial coefficients are determined and any further computation will involve use of factorial polynomials. Hence a program for using Gregory–Newton polynomials for interpolation or extrapolation must contain a routine for factorial polynomial evaluation, which, however, offers no particular difficulty.

An important consideration in connection with a difference table and the polynomial coefficients derived therefrom is that of round-off error. Consider the following example.

EXAMPLE 3.4.2   Given the following table of values of e^{-x}, find the 4th degree Gregory–Newton polynomial which passes through these five points and discuss the round-off error of the polynomial coefficient.

Solution

x	$y = e^{-x}$	Δy	$\Delta^2 y$	$\Delta^3 y$	$\Delta^4 y$
0.1	0.9048				
		−0.0861			
0.2	0.8187		0.0082		
		−0.0779		−0.0008	
0.3	0.7408		0.0074		0.0001
		−0.0705		−0.0007	
0.4	0.6703		0.0067		
		−0.0638			
0.5	0.6065				

The 4th degree Gregory–Newton polynomial is

$$P_4(x) = 0.9048 - 0.0861\, u^{[1]} + \frac{0.0082}{2}\, u^{[2]} - \frac{0.0008}{6}\, u^{[3]} + \frac{0.0001}{24}\, u^{[4]},$$

where $u = \dfrac{x - 0.1}{0.1} = 10x - 1$.

Since the table was constructed using a four place table, the entries in the y column are accurate to within ±0.00005. The maximum round-off errors in the Δy's in then of order (±0.00005)(2) or ±0.0001. In the third column, the possible round-off errors are again doubled or are of the order of ±0.0002. The maximum possible round-off error in the last column of the table is then ±0.0008, which indicates that the fourth column term is not trustworthy.

In general, where the round-off error of the tabulated y's are known, the maximum possible round-off error in $\Delta^k y$ is of order $(p \times 10^{-q}) \cdot 2^k$ if the round-off error of the tabulated values are of the order $p \times 10^{-q}$. This fact provides some basis for judgment in selecting the initial data, where a choice is possible.

An analysis of the accuracy of a result found by means of a Gregory–Newton polynomial should include not only a consideration of the remainder term, discussed in the next section, but also the round-off error when known.

Exercises

Find the maximum inaccuracy in $P_4(0.6)$ of Example 3.4.2 due to the inaccuracy of the tabulated values of y.

3.5 Remainder Term for the Gregory–Newton Formula

If a polynomial is to be used to approximate a given function or set of data, it is certainly desirable to have some measure of accuracy of this approximation. Since the Gregory–Newton polynomial, $P_n(x)$, of Equation 3.4.5 passes through the $n + 1$ points, (x_i, y_i), then if the y_i are values of a given function $f(x)$, at $x = x_i$, it follows that

$$P_n(x_i) = f(x_i), \qquad i = 0, 1, \ldots, n. \qquad (3.5.1)$$

In this sense, namely, that $P_n(x_i) = f(x_i)$ at $i = 0, 1, \ldots, n$; $P_n(x)$ approximates $f(x)$. The approximation is in error by zero at the $(n + 1)$ points specified but further information must be sought for the error in the approximation at any other point.

Since $P_n(x)$ has the same values as $f(x)$ at the $n + 1$ tabulated points $x_0, x_1, \ldots, x_n$, the function $f(x)$ can be expressed as

$$f(x) = P_n(x) + R(x), \qquad (3.5.2)$$

where $R(x)$ is some function which is zero at the same $n + 1$ tabulated points, $x_0, x_1, \ldots, x_n$, at which $f(x)$ and $P_n(x)$ agree. The function $R(x)$ can therefore be expressed in the form

$$R(x) = K(x)(x - x_0)(x - x_1) \cdots (x - x_n) \qquad (3.5.3)$$

for some function $K(x)$, and Equation 3.5.2 can be written as

$$f(x) = P_n(x) + K(x)(x - x_0) \cdots (x - x_n). \qquad (3.5.4)$$

In order to express Equation 3.5.2 entirely in terms of $P_n(x)$ and $f(x)$ it is desirable to express $R(x)$ as a function of $f(x)$ or its derivatives. To this end let a function $W(t)$ be defined as

$$W(t) = f(t) - P_n(t) - K(x)(t - x_0)(t - x_1) \cdots (t - x_n). \quad (3.5.5)$$

Notice that K is still a function of x and not of t. The function $W(t)$ vanishes at the $n + 1$ values $x_0, x_1, \ldots, x_n$ and in addition at any real value of x for which $f(x)$ is defined. Let x' be a particular value of x, distinct from $x_0, x_1, \ldots, x_n$, in the region of definition of $f(x)$ at which $f(x)$ is to be evaluated. The function $W(t)$ has at least $n + 2$ real zeros, $x', x_0, x_1, \ldots, x_n$, and, assuming that $f(t)$ possesses sufficient derivatives, by Rolle's theorem, $W'(t)$ has at least $n + 1$ real zeros lying between the largest and smallest of the $n + 2$ values $x', x_0, x_1, \ldots, x_n$. Likewise each derivative $W^{(i)}(t)$ has at least $n + 2 - i$ real zeros in the same interval and hence $W^{(n+1)}(t)$ has at least one real zero, $t = p$, in the interval.

Recall that, for a polynomial of degree k with the leading coefficient a_k, the kth derivative is a constant equal to $k! a_k$ and the $(k + 1)$st derivative is zero. Then, since the quantity multiplying $K(x)$ in Equation 3.5.4 is a polynomial of degree $n + 1$, the $(n + 1)$st derivative of $W(t)$, as defined in Equation 3.5.5, is

$$W^{(n+1)}(t) = f^{(n+1)}(t) - K(x)(n + 1)!. \qquad (3.5.6)$$

Therefore, since $W^{(n+1)}(p) = 0$,

$$K(x) = \frac{f^{(n+1)}(p)}{(n + 1)!}. \qquad (3.5.7)$$

Equation 3.5.4 can be expressed as

$$f(x) = P_n(x) + \frac{f^{(n+1)}(p)}{(n + 1)!}(x - x_0)(x - x_1) \cdots (x - x_n), \qquad (3.5.8)$$

where the last term is the remainder term, $R(x)$. Here p is some value of x lying in the range determined by $x_0, x_1, \ldots, x_n$ and the value of x at which $f(x)$ is evaluated.

Since

$$u = \frac{x - x_0}{h} \quad \text{and} \quad x_i = x_0 + ih \qquad (3.5.9)$$

for equal intervals on x, then

$$x - x_i = x - x_0 - ih = h(u - i) \qquad (3.5.10)$$

and

$$(x - x_0)(x - x_1) \cdots (x - x_n) = h^{n+1}u(u - 1) \cdots (u - n)$$
$$= h^{n+1}u^{[n+1]}. \qquad (3.5.11)$$

Thus the remainder term can be written as

$$R(x) = \frac{f^{(n+1)}(p)}{(n + 1)!} h^{n+1}u^{[n+1]}. \qquad (3.5.12)$$

Substituting Equations 3.4.5 and 3.5.12 into Equation 3.5.2 gives

$$f(x) = y_0 + u^{[1]}\Delta y_0 + \frac{u^{[2]}\Delta^2 y_0}{2!} + \cdots + \frac{u^{[n-1]}\Delta^{n-1}y_0}{(n - 1)!}$$
$$\qquad (3.5.13)$$
$$+ u^{[n]}\frac{\Delta^n y_0}{n!} + \frac{h^{n+1}}{(n + 1)!}u^{[n+1]}f^{(n+1)}(p),$$

where p is in the interval defined by $x_0, x_1, \ldots, x_n$, and x. This is the *Gregory–Newton formula with remainder*.

Note that, in general, p is *some* value of x for which $f(x)$ is defined and u is simply a function of x. Hence, in general, the best that can be done is to attempt to find an upper bound on the term

$$|R(x)| = \left| \frac{h^{n+1}}{(n + 1)!} u^{[n+1]}f^{(n+1)}(p) \right|. \qquad (3.5.14)$$

If $f(x)$ is known analytically, a bound on the derivative term may be possible. The bound on $u^{[n+1]}$ will depend on the range of x. Once an interval on x is selected, it may be possible to determine a bound on u, and hence on $u^{[n+1]}$.

If Equation 3.5.13 is being used to find the value of $f(x)$ for a specified x, as in interpolation or extrapolation, then u is determined, the interval in which p lies is also determined, and only the derivative is unknown. If $f(x)$ is a function which is known analytically and if a bound on $|f^{(n+1)}(p)|$ exists and can be found, then a bound on $R(x)$ is determined.

EXAMPLE 3.5.1   From the following tabulation, find the Gregory–Newton formula with remainder. Use this formula to approximate $f(0.03)$ and $f(1.0)$ and discuss the error or remainder term.

x	$y = f(x)$	Δy	$\Delta^2 y$	$\Delta^3 y$	$\Delta^4 y$
0	0				
		0.019997			
0.02	0.019997		−0.000007		
		0.019990		−0.000006	
0.04	0.039987		−0.000013		−0.000009
		0.019977		−0.000015	
0.06	0.059964		−0.000028		
		0.019949			
0.08	0.079913				

Solution: By Equation 3.4.5

$$P_4(x) = 0 + 0.019997u - \frac{0.000007}{2}u^{[2]} - \frac{0.000006}{6}u^{[3]} - \frac{0.000009}{24}u^{[4]}$$

$$= 0.019997u - 0.0000035u^{[2]} - 0.000001u^{[3]} - 0.000000375u^{[4]}.$$

The remainder term is, by Equation 3.5.12,

$$R(x) = \frac{f^{(5)}(p)}{5!}h^5 u^{[5]} = \frac{2^5 \times 10^{-10}}{120}f^{(5)}(p)u^{[5]}.$$

From the tabulated values alone, nothing can be said about $f^{[5]}(p)$ and until a value of x or at least an interval on x is specified, nothing can be said about a bound on $u^{[5]}$.

If

$$x = 0.03, \qquad u = \frac{0.03}{0.02} = 1.5,$$

then

$$P_n(0.03) = 0.019997(1.5) - 0.0000035(1.5)(0.5)$$
$$+ 0.000001(1.5)(0.5)(-0.5) -$$
$$- 0.000000375(1.5)(0.5)(-0.5)(-1.5)$$
$$= 0.0299923.$$

The remainder term is

$$R(0.03) = \frac{2^5 \times 10^{-10}}{120}(1.5)(0.5)(-0.5)(-1.5)(-2.5)f^{(5)}(p)$$
$$= -3.75 \times 10^{-11}f^{(5)}(p),$$

where p is now in the interval $(0, 0.08)$. But without some knowledge of the analytical nature of $f(x)$ there is still no available bound on this error term.

With the added information that the tabulated values of $f(x)$ actually correspond to the function $y = \sin x$, the picture is altered. Now, since all orders of derivatives of $f(x)$ will be either $\sin x$ or $\cos x$, the upper bound on the magnitudes of all derivatives will be 1 and the error $|R(0.03)| \le 3.75 \times 10^{-11}$.

For $x = 1.0$, $u = 5$. Then

$$R(1.0) = \frac{2^5 \times 10^{-10}}{120}(50)(49)(48)(47)(46)f^{(5)}(p) = 0.00678f^{(5)}(p).$$

Since $|f^{(5)}(p)| \le 1$ for p in any interval on x, the magnitude of error of $P_n(1.0)$ is less than or equal to 0.00678 and in this case the Gregory–Newton formula gives an accuracy for extrapolation much less than that for interpolation within the tabulation.

With the information that the tabulated values are values of $\sin x$, the error analysis can and should include some consideration of round-off errors. Since tabulated values are from six-place tables, the round-off error in $f(x)$ is of the order of 5×10^{-7}. The maximum round-off errors are in general, then, as shown in the following tabulation.

$f(x)$	Δy	$\Delta^2 y$	$\Delta^3 y$	$\Delta^4 y$
5×10^{-7}	10^{-6}	2×10^{-6}	4×10^{-6}	8×10^{-6}

However, since $\sin 0 = 0$, the error terms for $\Delta^k y$ are as follows.

y_0	Δy_0	$\Delta^2 y_0$	$\Delta^3 y_0$	$\Delta^4 y_0$
0	5×10^{-7}	1.5×10^{-6}	3.5×10^{-6}	7.5×10^{-6}

The maximum error added to $P_4(x)$ due to round-off is, then, given by

$$0 + |0.5u \times 10^{-6}| + \left| \frac{1.5u^{[2]} \times 10^{-6}}{2} \right| + \left| \frac{3.5u^{[3]} \times 10^{-6}}{3!} \right|$$
$$+ \left| \frac{7.5u^{[4]} \times 10^{-6}}{4!} \right|.$$

For $x = 0.03$ and hence $u = 1.5$, this error is

$$10^{-6} \left[0.5(1.5) + \frac{1.5(1.5)(0.5)}{2} + \left| \frac{3.5(1.5)(0.5)(-0.5)}{6} \right| \right.$$
$$\left. + \frac{7.5(1.5)(0.5)(-0.5)(-1.5)}{24} \right]$$
$$= 1.70703 \times 10^{-6}.$$

This possible error is much larger than the remainder term. While it is not likely that round-off errors will all add and thus give the worst possible error, this example serves to point up a reason why the remainder term does not give the whole answer to the problem of accuracy.

EXAMPLE 3.5.2   Tabulate the function

$$f(x) = x^5 - 10x^4 + 35x^3 - 50x^2 + 25x + 50$$

at $x = 0, 1, 2, 3, 4$ and find the polynomial of degree 4 or less which approximates the given function according to the Gregory–Newton criterion.

Solution: The table constructed on the values of $f(x)$ obtained by direct substitution into the equation is as follows.

x	y	Δy	$\Delta^2 y$
0	50		
		1	
1	51		0
		1	
2	52		0
		1	
3	53		0
		1	
4	54		

The Gregory–Newton polynomial is then

$$P_m(x) = x + 50, \qquad m \leq 4.$$

Thus, in this case the *unique* polynomial of degree *four* or *less* turns out to be a first degree polynomial.

The value of $P_m(x)$ for $x = 5$ is 55 whereas the value found by substitution of $x = 5$ into the original $f(x)$ is 175.

The error term for $P_m(x)$ is

$$R(x) = \frac{1}{5!} u^{[5]} f^{(5)}(p).$$

Since $f^{(5)}(x) = 5!$ for $f(x)$ a 5th degree polynomial, for $x = u = 5$, $R(5) = (1/5!)\, 5!\, 5! = 5! = 120$, which is the exact error obtained by evaluating $f(5)$ and $P_m(5)$ and subtracting.

Special note should be taken of the fact that while the actual degree of the approximating polynomial may be *less than* m, the m used in the remainder term is determined by the number of values of $f(x)$ in the table and not by the actual degree of the Gregory–Newton polynomial, as is illustrated in the last example.

Problems

3.1   Construct a difference table for values of e^{-x} for $0.1 \le x \le 0.2$ with $h = 0.02$.

3.2   Construct a difference table for values of $\sin x$ for $0 \le x \le 0.5°$ with $h = 0.05°$.

3.3   Show that $u^{[n]}(u - n)^{[m]} = u^{[n+m]}$.

3.4   Show that if $n > m$,

$$\frac{u^{[n]}}{u^{[m]}} = (u - m)^{[n-m]}.$$

3.5   Show that, for m and n any two positive integers,

$$m^{[n]} \begin{cases} = 0 & \text{when } m < n, \\ = n! & \text{when } m = n, \\ = \dfrac{m!}{(m - n)!} & \text{when } m > n. \end{cases}$$

3.6   If $u^{[-k]}$ is defined as

$$u^{[-k]} = \frac{1}{(u + 1)(u + 2) \cdots (u + k)},$$

show that

$$\Delta u^{[-k]} = -k u^{[-(k+1)]}.$$

3.7   Express the polynomial

$$P_5(x) = x^5 + 3x^4 - 7x^3 + 2x^2 - x + 4$$

in terms of factorial polynomials, as in Example 3.3.1.

3.8   Express the polynomial

$$P_4(x) = x^4 + x^2 + 5$$

in terms of factorial polynomials, as in Example 3.3.1.

3.9   Show, by extending the table in Problem 3.7, that for this mth degree polynomial the mth differences are constants and the $(m + 1)$st differences are zero.

3.10   Repeat Problem 3.9 for the polynomial of Problem 3.8.

3.11   (a) Find the Gregory–Newton formula for $f(x) = e^{-x}$ through 4 points with $x_0 = 0$ and $h = 0.02$.

(b) Use the polynomial in Part (a) to evaluate e^{-x} for $x = 0.03$, $x = 1.0$ and $x = 1.4$ and give a complete analysis of the error term in each case.

3.12   Repeat Problem 3.11 for $f(x) = e^x$.

3.13   (a) Tabulate values of the function

$$f(x) = x^4 - 6x^3 + 12x^2 - 9x + 5$$

for $x = 0, 1, 2$ and 3, and find the Gregory–Newton polynomial $P_3(x)$ for this tabulation.

(b) Use the polynomial found in Part (a) to find $P_3(x)$ for $x = 1.5$ and $x = 4$ and give a complete error analysis in each case.

3.14   Show that $\Delta(f(x) + g(x)) = \Delta f(x) + \Delta g(x)$ and $\Delta(f(x)g(x)) = f(x + h)\,\Delta g(x) + g(x)\,\Delta f(x)$.

CHAPTER 4

Numerical Integration

ONE APPROACH to numerical integration is the approximation of a given function, $f(x)$, by a polynomial, $P_m(x)$, and the integration of the polynomial rather than of the given function. The value of this method is apparent, particularly when the given function is difficult to integrate.

The polynomial used to approximate the given function, $f(x)$, may be any one of a number of polynomials of the types considered in Chapters 3 and 7. In this chapter, a polynomial derived by use of difference tables is considered, specifically the Gregory–Newton polynomial. A second kind of numerical integration, Gaussian quadrature, is discussed in Chapter 8.

4.1 Quadrature Formulas

The problem of numerical integration is to evaluate

$$\int_a^b f(x)\, dx \qquad (4.1.1)$$

when the indefinite integral

$$F(x) = \int f(x)\, dx \qquad (4.1.2)$$

is not readily obtained.

The method to be followed in this chapter is to replace $f(x)$ by a polynomial $P_n(x)$ which is the same as $f(x)$ at $x_0, x_1, \ldots, x_n$, where these values have been selected so that $a = x_0$ and $b = x_n$. Thus, the integral $\int_a^b f(x)\, dx$ is replaced by $\int_{x_0}^{x_n} P_n(x)\, dx$ with $a = x_0$, $b = x_n$. An expression thus obtained to approximate $\int_a^b f(x)\, dx$ is called a *closed quadrature formula*.

A second kind of quadrature formula, the open type, is useful primarily in the development of predictor-corrector formulas for the solution of differential equations and is discussed in that context in Chapter 5.

Exercises

1. Approximate e^x by a polynomial $P(x)$ such that $P(x_i) = e^{x_i}$ for $x_i = \dfrac{i}{4}$, $i = 0, 1, 2, 3, 4$. Then approximate $\displaystyle\int_0^1 e^x \, dx$ by $\displaystyle\int_0^1 P(x) \, dx$.

2. Since $\displaystyle\int_0^1 e^x \, dx = e - 1$, then $e \approx 1 + \displaystyle\int_0^1 P(x) \, dx$ is an approximation to e. Compare this approximation with $e \approx P(1)$.

4.2 Quadrature Formulas Using Gregory–Newton Polynomials

Quadrature formulas can be derived by using a finite difference table and one of the approximating polynomials derived from this table; e.g., the Gregory–Newton polynomial.

Using the Gregory–Newton polynomial, without the error term, on an interval (x_0, x_m), the approximation to the integral is

$$I(x_m) = \int_{x_0}^{x_m} f(x) \, dx \approx \int_{x_0}^{x_m} \left[f(x_0) + \Delta f(x_0) u^{[1]} + \frac{\Delta^2 f(x_0)}{2} u^{[2]} \right.$$
$$\left. + \cdots + \frac{\Delta^m f(x_0)}{m!} u^{[m]} \right] dx. \quad (4.2.1)$$

Since u is defined as $u = \dfrac{x - x_0}{h}$, then $dx = h \, du$. When $x = x_0$, $u = 0$ and when $x = x_m$, $u = \dfrac{x_m - x_0}{h} = m$. The integral of Equation 4.2.1 can be written as

$$I(x_m) \approx h \int_0^m \left[f(x_0) + \Delta f(x_0) u^{[1]} + \cdots + \frac{\Delta^m f(x_0)}{m!} u^{[m]} \right] du. \quad (4.2.2)$$

The integration in this last equation is a straightforward operation and is illustrated in the following example.

EXAMPLE 4.2.1 Use the Gregory–Newton polynomial (without the error term) to derive a quadrature formula using two points.

Solution: The difference table for two points is

TABLE 4.2.1

x	$f(x)$	$\Delta f(x)$
x_0	f_0	
		$f_1 - f_0$
x_1	f_1	

The Gregory–Newton polynomial for this tabulation is

$$P_1(x) = f_0 + (f_1 - f_0)u^{[1]}. \tag{4.2.3}$$

The integral, $I(x_m)$, can now be expressed as

$$I(x_1) = \int_{x_0}^{x_1} f(x)\, dx \approx h \int_0^1 \left[f_0 + (f_1 - f_0)u^{[1]} \right] du$$

$$= h \left[f_0 u + \frac{(f_1 - f_0)u^2}{2} \right]_0^1 = \frac{h}{2}[f_0 + f_1]. \tag{4.2.4}$$

The formula in Equation 4.2.4 is one of a general class discussed in a following section and is called the trapezoidal rule.

The formula 4.2.4 is general in that it can be used to approximate $\int_{x_0}^{x} f(t)\, dt$ for any integrable function, $f(x)$.

EXAMPLE 4.2.2   Use Equation 4.2.4 to approximate

$$\int_{1.0}^{1.1} \ln x \, dx.$$

Solution: In this case

$$x_0 = 1,$$
$$x_1 = 1.1,$$
$$h = x_1 - x_0 = 0.1.$$

Hence

$$\int_{1.0}^{1.1} \ln x \, dx \approx \frac{h}{2}[f(1.1) + f(1)]$$

$$= \frac{0.1}{2}[\ln 1.1 + \ln 1] = \frac{\ln 1.1}{20}.$$

The question as to the accuracy of the answer given by Equation 4.2.4 immediately arises. This question is answered in the next section.

Exercise

Determine the accuracy of the approximation

$$\int_{1.0}^{1.1} \ln x \, dx \approx \frac{\ln 1.1}{20}$$

by means of actual integration.

4.3   The Error Term in Quadrature Formulas

In Equation 4.2.1, $f(x)$ is approximated by a polynomial, $P_m(x)$. It is shown in Chapter 3 that if a certain remainder, $R_m(x)$, is added to $P_m(x)$,

$f(x) = P_m(x) + R_m(x)$. Then in Equation 4.2.1,

$$\int_{x_0}^{x_m} f(x)\, dx = \int_{x_0}^{x_m} P_m(x)\, dx + \int_{x_0}^{x_m} R_m(x)\, dx. \tag{4.3.1}$$

The error, or discrepancy between the true value of the integral and the value given by Equation 4.2.2, is then $\int_{x_0}^{x_m} R_m(x)\, dx$, which in terms of the variable u is

$$E_m = \frac{h^{m+2}}{(m+1)!} \int_0^m u^{[m+1]} f^{(m+1)}(\delta_m)\, du. \tag{4.3.2}$$

Since δ_m is dependent on u, the integral in this last equation cannot be evaluated directly. It can be shown,* however, that this integral takes on one of the two forms

$$E_m = \frac{h^{m+2} f^{(m+1)}(\delta)}{(m+1)!} \int_0^m u^{[m+1]}\, du \qquad (x_0 < \delta < x_m) \qquad (m \text{ odd}) \tag{4.3.3}$$

or

$$E_m = \frac{h^{m+3} f^{(m+2)}(\delta)}{(m+2)!} \int_0^m \left(u - \frac{m}{2}\right) u^{[m+1]}\, du \tag{4.3.4}$$

$$(x_0 < \delta < x_m) \qquad (m \text{ even})$$

EXAMPLE 4.3.1   Derive the error term for the trapezoidal rule given by Equation 4.2.4.

Solution: Since, for the formula in question, $m = 1$, Equation 4.3.3 is required. The error term is then

$$
\begin{aligned}
E_1 &= \frac{h^3 f''(\delta)}{2!} \int_0^1 u^{[2]}\, du \\
&= \frac{h^3 f''(\delta)}{2} \left[\frac{u^3}{3} - \frac{u^2}{2}\right]_0^1 = -\frac{h^3 f''(\delta)}{12} \qquad (x_0 < \delta < x_1). \tag{4.3.5}
\end{aligned}
$$

EXAMPLE 4.3.2   Find the error term for Example 4.2.2.

Solution: Since $f(x) = \ln x$, then $f''(x) = -1/x^2$. However, the exact value of δ which appears in Equation 4.3.5 is not known. As a result, a bound on the error term is sought, that is, a bound on

$$|E_1| = \frac{h^3}{12} |f''(\delta)|.$$

---

* See Hamming, R. W., *Numerical Methods for Scientists and Engineers*, McGraw-Hill Book Company, New York, 1962, Sections 11.3 and 11.4.

Since $|f''(x)| = \left|\dfrac{1}{x^2}\right|$ is a decreasing function as x increases, the maximum of $|f''(x)|$ in the interval (1.1.1) occurs at $x = 1$. Hence

$$|f''(\delta)| < 1 \qquad \text{for } 1 < \delta < 1.1$$

and

$$|E_1| < \frac{(0.1)^3}{12} = 0.000083.$$

Thus, the result $\dfrac{\ln 1.1}{20}$ differs from $\displaystyle\int_1^{1.} \ln\, dx$ by at most 0.000083, so that the result is accurate to about four decimal places.

Exercise

Compare the error term just obtained for the approximation to $\displaystyle\int_1^{1.1} \ln x\, dx$ with the error obtained in the problem at the end of Section 4.2.

4.4   Quadrature Formulas over Several Intervals—Summing

If the interval over which integration is to be performed is divided into equal increments small enough to assure a reasonable degree of accuracy, the number of points, and hence the degree of the approximating polynomial, will be high. As a result the calculation of the polynomial can be seriously affected by rounding error. Furthermore, if for each integral, $\displaystyle\int_a^b f(x)\, dx$, a polynomial of sufficiently high degree must be selected so as to obtain accuracy, it could well be the case that for each (a, b) and $f(x)$ a new polynomial would have to be derived. In order to limit the number of polynomials which must be derived, and at the same time have the increment on x, that is, h, small, the total interval is divided into subintervals. The selected quadrature formula is applied to each of these subintervals separately and the results summed to give the integral over the total interval.

Consider Figure 4.4.1. The area under the curve, $y = f(x)$, over the total interval (x_0, x_n) is shown divided into five parts, corresponding to five subintervals on x, by means of the heavy vertical lines.

The area of each part is determined by integrating, over the subinterval, an approximating polynomial of degree m determined from the $m + 1$ tabulated points in the subinterval.

In general, the integral $I(x_n)$ over an interval, (x_0, x_n), in terms of the integrals over subintervals of $(x_{im}, x_{(i+1)m})$, may be approximated by

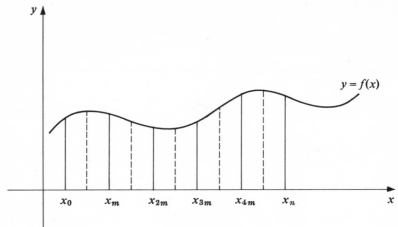

FIGURE 4.4.1

Equation 4.2.2 as

$$I(x_n) \approx h \left\{ \int_0^m \left[f(x_0) + \Delta f(x_0) \, u^{[1]} + \cdots + \frac{\Delta^m f(x_0)}{m!} \, u^{[m]} \right] du \right.$$

$$+ \int_m^{2m} \left[f(x_m) + \Delta f(x_m) \, u^{[1]} + \cdots + \frac{\Delta^m f(x_m)}{m!} \, u^{[m]} \right] du + \cdots$$

$$\left. + \int_{km}^n f(x_{km}) + \Delta f(x_{km}) \, u^{[1]} + \cdots + \frac{\Delta^m f(x_{km})}{m!} \, u^{[m]} \right] du \right\},$$

$$(4.4.1)$$

where

$$n = m(k + 1). \qquad (4.4.2)$$

While Equation 4.4.1 may appear to be rather complex, its actual application is very simple, as is shown in the following example.

EXAMPLE 4.4.1   Apply the trapezoidal rule over n subintervals to find an approximation to the integral

$$I = \int_{x_0}^{x_n} f(x) \, dx. \qquad (4.4.3)$$

Solution: First replace Equation 4.4.3 by

$$\int_{x_0}^{x_n} f(x) \, dx = \int_{x_0}^{x_1} f(x) \, dx + \int_{x_1}^{x_2} f(x) \, dx + \cdots + \int_{x_{n-1}}^{x_n} f(x) \, dx. \quad (4.4.4)$$

By Equation 4.2.4 the integrals on the right side of Equation 4.4.4 are approximated as

$$\int_{x_0}^{x_1} f(x)\, dx \approx \frac{h}{2}\, [f_0 + f_1]$$

$$\int_{x_1}^{x_2} f(x)\, dx \approx \frac{h}{2}\, [f_1 + f_2]$$

(4.4.5)

.

.

.

$$\int_{x_{n-1}}^{x_n} f(x)\, dx \approx \frac{h}{2}\, [f_{n-1} + f_n]$$

The sum over the total interval is

$$I(x_n) = \int_{x_0}^{x_n} f(x)\, dx \approx \frac{h}{2}\, [f_0 + f_1) + (f_1 + f_2) + \cdots + (f_{n-1} + f_n)]$$

(4.4.6)

or

$$I(x_n) \approx \frac{h}{2}\, [f_0 + 2f_1 + 2f_2 + \cdots + 2f_{n-1} + f_n].$$ (4.4.7)

The error formula corresponding to Equation 4.4.1 will be

$$E_n = \sum_{j=0}^{k} \frac{h^{m+2} f^{(m+1)}(\delta_j)}{(m+1)!} \int_{jm}^{(j+1)m} u^{[m+1]}\, du \qquad (m \text{ odd}) \qquad (4.4.8)$$

or

$$E_n = \sum_{j=0}^{k} \frac{h^{m+3} f^{(m+2)}(\delta_j)}{(m+2)!} \int_{jm}^{(j+1)m} \left(u - \frac{m}{2}\right) u^{[m+1]}\, du \qquad (m \text{ even}), \quad (4.4.9)$$

where $x_{jm} < \delta_j < x_{(j+1)m}$.

Since the integrals in Equation 4.4.8 are all the same (see Problem 1) and similarly for the integrals in Equation 4.4.9, the error formula can be written as

$$E_n = K_1 \sum_{j=0}^{k} f^{(m+1)}(\delta_j) \qquad (4.4.10)$$

or

$$E_n = K_2 \sum_{j=0}^{k} f^{m+2}(\delta_j), \qquad (4.4.11)$$

where K_1 and K_2 are constants.

If the derivatives in Equations 4.4.10 and 4.4.11 are continuous and hence bounded in the closed interval (x_0, x_n) and if $f^{[m+i]}(\delta)$, $i = 1, 2$, are such that

$$|f^{(m+i)}(\delta_j)| \leq |f^{(m+i)}(\delta)| \qquad \text{for every } j, \qquad (4.4.12)$$

then

$$|E_n| \leq |K_i(k + 1) f^{[m+i]}(\delta)|. \qquad (4.4.13)$$

EXAMPLE 4.4.2   Find the error term for the trapezoidal rule over the total interval (x_0, x_n) for $n = k + 1$.

Solution: By Equation 4.3.5 the error term for one subinterval is given by

$$E_1 = -\frac{h^3 f''(\delta_0)}{12} \qquad (x_0 < \delta_0 < x_1). \qquad (4.4.14)$$

If $f''(\delta)$ is a bound on $f''(x)$ in the interval (x_0, x_n), as defined in Equation 4.4.12, the error term for the total interval is

$$|E_n| < \frac{h^3}{12} n \, |f''(\delta)| \qquad (4.4.15)$$

or, since $nh = x_n - x_0$,

$$E_n \approx -\frac{h^2}{12} (x_n - x_0) f''(\delta) \, (x_0 < \delta < x_n). \qquad (4.4.16)$$

The complete formula for the trapezoidal rule over an interval (x_0, x_n) is

$$I(x_n) = \int_{x_0}^{x_n} f(x) \, dx \approx \frac{h}{2} [f + 2f_1 + \cdots + 2f_{n-1} + f_n]$$

$$- \frac{h^2}{12} (x_n - x_0) f''(\delta). \quad (4.4.17)$$

In fact, it can be shown that for some δ, Equation 4.4.17 becomes an identity, not an approximation.

Exercises

1. If $\int_a^b f(x) \, dx$ is to be approximated by

$$\int_{x_0}^{x_1} [f(x_0) + \Delta f(x_0) \, u] \, dx + \int_{x_1}^{x_2} [f(x_1) + \Delta f(x_1) \, u] \, dx$$

$$+ \cdots + \int_{x_{n-1}}^{x} [f(x_{n-1}) + \Delta f(x_{n-1}) u] \, dx,$$

then the error term is, by Equation 4.3.3,

$$\frac{h^3}{2!} \left\{ f''(\delta_0) \int_{x_0}^{x_1} u^{[2]} \, dx + f''(\delta_1) \int_{x_1}^{x_2} u^{[2]} \, dx + \cdots + f''(\delta_{n-1}) \int_{x_{n-1}}^{x_n} u^{[2]} \, dx \right\},$$

where $x_i < \delta_i < x_{i+1}$, $i = 0, 1, 2, \ldots, n - 1$. Note, however, that the $u^{[2]}$ in each integral is different from the $u^{[2]}$ in the other integrals. That is, in $\int_{x_{i-1}}^{x_i} u^{[2]} \, dx$, $u = \dfrac{x - x_{i-1}}{h}$. Show that $\int_{x_{i-1}}^{x_i} u^{[2]} \, dx = \int_{x_{j-1}}^{x_j} u^{[2]} \, dx$ for any i and j from 0 through $n - 1$.

2. If $f''(x)$ is continuous over the interval (x_0, x_n) and if $x_j \leq \delta_j \leq x_{j+1}$, $= 0, \ldots, n - 1$, show that $\sum_{j=0}^{n-1} f''(\delta_j) = nf''(\delta)$ for some δ in the range

$x_0 \le \delta \le x_n$. Hence, prove that the approximation in Equation 4.4.17 is an identity for some δ.

4.5 Newton-Cotes Formulas

One class of quadrature formulas is characterized by the fact that the integration extends from the first to the last ordinate employed in the formula. These closed formulas are known as the Newton-Cotes formulas.

The trapezoidal rule derived in the preceding section is one of the Newton-Cotes formulas. One other Newton-Cotes formula which is very commonly used is derived in the following way.

Consider the following difference table, for a subinterval of length $2h$.

TABLE 4.5.1

x	$f(x)$	$\Delta f(x)$	$\Delta^2 f(x)$
x_0	f_0		
		$f_1 - f_0$	
x_1	f_1		$f_2 - 2f_1 + f_0$
		$f_2 - f_1$	
x_2	f_2		

The Gregory-Newton polynomial and remainder derived from this tabulation is

$$f(x) = f_0 + (f_1 - f_0) u^{[1]} + \frac{(f_2 - 2f_1 + f_0)}{2} u^{[2]}$$

$$+ \frac{h^3}{3!} u^{[3]} f'''(\delta) \qquad (x_0 < \delta < x_2), \quad (4.5.1)$$

and the integral is

$$I(x_0, x_2) = \int_{x_0}^{x_2} f(x)\, dx = h \int_0^2 \left[f_0 + (f_1 - f_0) u^{[1]} + \frac{f_2 - 2f_1 + f_0}{2} u^{[2]} \right] du$$

$$+ h \int_0^2 \frac{h^3}{3!} u^{[3]} f'''(\delta)\, du. \quad (4.5.2)$$

The first integral on the right side of Equation 4.5.2 is

$$h \int_0^2 \left[f_0 + (f_1 - f_0) u^{[1]} + \frac{(f_2 - 2f_1 + f_0)}{2} u^{[2]} \right] du$$

$$= h \left[f_0 u + (f_1 - f_0) \frac{u^2}{2} + \frac{f_2 - 2f_1 + f_0}{2} \left(\frac{u^3}{3} - \frac{u^2}{2} \right) \right]_0^2$$

$$= \frac{h}{3} [f_0 + 4f_1 + f_2]. \quad (4.5.3)$$

Since m is even, Equation 4.3.4 gives the error term as

$$E_2 = \frac{h^5}{4!} f^{iv}(\delta_0) \int_0^2 (u-1) u^{[3]} \, du$$

$$= \frac{h^5}{24} f^{iv}(\delta_0) \left[\frac{u^5}{5} - u^4 + \frac{5u^3}{3} - u^2 \right]_0^2$$

$$= \frac{-h^5}{90} f^{iv}(\delta_0) \qquad (x_0 < \delta_0 < x_2). \qquad (4.5.4)$$

Combining Equations 4.5.3 and 4.5.4 gives

$$\int_{x_0}^{x_2} f(x) \, dx = \frac{h}{3} [f_0 + 4f_1 + f_2] - \frac{h^5}{90} f^{iv}(\delta_0) \qquad (x_0 < \delta_0 < x_2) \quad (4.5.5)$$

as the integral over one subinterval of length $2h$. If this result is summed over the total interval (x_0, x_n) or $\frac{n}{2}$ subintervals, for n an even number, it can be shown that

$$\int_{x_0}^{x_n} f(x) \, dx = \frac{h}{3} [f_0 + 4f_1 + 2f_2 + 4f_3 + \cdots + 4f_{n-1} + f_n] - \frac{h^5}{90} f^{iv}(\delta) \frac{n}{2}$$

$$(4.5.6)$$

or, since $\dfrac{x_n - x_0}{h} = n$,

$$\int_{x_0}^{x_n} f(x) \, dx = \frac{h}{3} [f_0 + 4f_1 + 2f_2 + \cdots + 4f_{n-1} + f_n] - \frac{h^4(x_n - x_0)}{180} f^{iv}(\delta),$$

$$(4.5.7)$$

where $x_0 < \delta < x_n$.

Equation 4.5.7 is called Simpson's one-third rule, or the parabolic rule, and is probably the most widely used of all the quadrature formulas.

In a similar manner, other formulas may be derived. Three such formulas are given without derivations.

Four-point formulas: Simpson's three-eighths rule
One interval

$$\int_{x_0}^{x_3} f(x) \, dx = \frac{3h}{8} (f_0 + 3f_1 + 3f_2 + f_3) - \frac{3h^5}{80} f^{iv}(\delta_0); \qquad (4.5.8)$$

$\dfrac{n}{3}$ intervals

$$\int_{x_0}^{x_n} f(x) \, dx = \frac{3h}{8} (f_0 + 3f_1 + 3f_2 + 2f_3 + 3f_4 + 3f_5 + 2f_6 + \cdots$$

$$+ 3f_{n-1} + f_n) - \frac{h^4(x_n - x_0)}{80} f^{iv}(\delta). \quad (4.5.9)$$

Five-point formulas
One interval

$$\int_{x_0}^{x_4} f(x)\, dx = \frac{2h}{45}(7f_0 + 32f_1 + 12f_2 + 32f_3 + 7f_4) - \frac{8h^7}{945}f^{(6)}(\delta_0); \quad (4.5.10)$$

$\frac{n}{4}$ intervals

$$\int_{x_0}^{x_n} f(x)\, dx = \frac{2h}{45}(7f_0 + 32f_1 + 12f_2 + 32f_3 + 14f_4 + 32f_5 + \cdots$$

$$+ 32f_{n-1} + 7f_n) - \frac{2h^6(x_n - x_0)}{945}f^{(6)}(\delta). \quad (4.5.11)$$

Seven-point formulas
One interval

$$\int_{x_0}^{x_6} f(x)\, dx = \frac{h}{140}(41f_0 + 216f_1 + 27f_2 + 272f_3 + 27f_4 + 216f_5 + 41f_6)$$

$$- \frac{9}{1400}h^9 f^{(8)}(\delta_0); \quad (4.5.12)$$

$\frac{n}{6}$ intervals

$$\int_{x_0}^{x_n} f(x)\, dx = \frac{h}{140}(41f_0 + 216f_1 + 27f_2 + 272f_3 + 27f_4 + 216f_5 + 82f_6$$

$$+ 216f_7 + 27f_8 + \cdots + 216f_{n-1} + 41f_n)$$

$$- \frac{3}{2800}h^8(x_n - x_0)f^{(8)}(\delta). \quad (4.5.13)$$

In general, the best quadrature formula to use is the one with the highest power of h in the remainder term. The reason for this is mainly connected with the round-off error involved. For as the number of function values, $f(x_i)$, needed increases, it can be expected that the round-off error will increase. Furthermore, the actual calculation time will be less with quadrature formulas for which the truncation error has a higher power of h since, for a specified accuracy, the higher power of h in the error term means that a larger h, and hence a smaller n, will satisfy the required conditions.

Comparing the formulas 4.4.17 and 4.5.13, if an error of ϵ can be tolerated, the h in Equation 4.4.17 would have to be of the order of $\sqrt{\epsilon}$, while the h of Equation 4.5.13 would be of the order of $\sqrt[8]{\epsilon}$. But since $n = (x_n - x_0)/h$, then n for Equation 4.4.17 would be the first integer greater than $(x_n - x_0)/\sqrt{\epsilon}$, while the n for Equation 4.5.13 would be the first multiple of 6 greater than $(x_n - x_0)/\sqrt[8]{\epsilon}$. To illustrate this point, suppose $x_n - x_0 = 1$ and $\epsilon = 10^{-8}$. Then Equation 4.4.17 would require about $1/\sqrt{10^{-8}} = 10{,}000$ function values; while Equation 4.5.13 would require 12 functional values since $1/\sqrt[8]{10^{-8}} = 10$.

EXAMPLE 4.5.1   As an illustration of the use of the Newton-Cotes formulas, find $\int_0^{1.0} e^{-x} \, dx$, using the trapezoidal rule and Simpson's rule for $h = 0.1$ and $h = 0.05$, and compare the error terms.

Solution: Using a four-place table of values for e^{-x}, the trapezoidal rule gives, from Equation 4.4.7, for $h = 0.1$ and $n = 10$,

$$\int_0^{1.0} e^{-x} \, dx \approx \frac{0.1}{2} [1 + 2(0.9048) + 2(0.8187) + 2(0.7408)$$
$$+ 2(0.6703) + 2(0.6065) + 2(0.5488) + 2(0.4966)$$
$$+ 2(0.4493) + 2(0.4066) + 0.3679]$$
$$\approx 0.63263.$$

Since, for $f(x) = e^{-x}$, $f''(x) = e^{-x}$, the maximum value of $f''(x)$ in the interval $0 \le x \le 1$ is 1, the error term is

$$|E_n| = \left| -\frac{1}{12} h^2 f''(\delta) \right| < \left| -\frac{h^2}{12} \right| = \left| -\frac{10^{-2}}{12} \right| = \frac{10^{-2}}{12}.$$

For $h = 0.05$ and $n = 20$, Equation 4.4.7 gives

$$\int_0^{1.0} e^{-x} \, dx \approx \frac{0.05}{2} [1 + 2(0.9512 + 0.9048 + 0.8607 + 0.8187$$
$$+ 0.7788 + 0.7408 + 0.7047 + 0.6703 + 0.6376 + 0.6065$$
$$+ 0.5769 + 0.5488 + 0.5220 + 0.4966 + 0.4724 + 0.4493$$
$$+ 0.4274 + 0.4066 + 0.3867) + 0.3679]$$
$$\approx 0.63224.$$

The error term for $h = 0.05$ is

$$|E_n| = \left| -\frac{1}{12} (0.05)^2 f''(\delta) \right| < \frac{25 \times 10^{-4}}{12}.$$

Using Simpson's rule to determine the value of the integral $\int_0^1 e^{-x} \, dx$ for $h = 0.1$ gives the following results:

$$\int_0^{1.0} e^{-x} \, dx = \frac{0.1}{3} [1 + 4(0.9048) + 2(0.8187) + 4(0.7408) + 2(0.6703)$$
$$+ 4(0.6065) + 2(0.5488) + 4(0.4966) + 2(0.4493)$$
$$+ 4(0.4066) + 0.3679] + E_n$$
$$= 0.63211 + E_n.$$

The magnitude of the error term is now

$$|E_n| = \left| -\frac{h^4(x_n - x_0)}{180} f^{iv}(\delta) \right| < \left| -\frac{(0.1)^4}{180} \right| = \left| -\frac{1}{18} \times 10^{-5} \right|.$$

For $h = 0.05$, Simpson's rule gives the following results:

$$\int_0^1 e^{-x}\, dx \approx \frac{0.05}{3}[37.9262] - \frac{(0.05)^4}{180} e^{-x} \approx 0.63210 - \frac{3125}{9} \times 10^{-10}.$$

It is apparent that in order to take advantage of the accuracy possible in applying a formula like Simpson's rule the functional values, in this case tabulated values of e^{-x}, must be accurate to more than four places. Examination of the error term shows that the method is capable of at least six decimal places of accuracy. The answer, 0.6321, is exactly the answer obtained by direct integration, using four-place tables. This exact agreement is, in fact, indicated by the error term.

EXAMPLE 4.5.2   Determine a value for h and n which will guarantee five decimal places of accuracy in the approximation to $\int_0^{1.0} e^{-x}\, dx$ by the trapezoidal rule.

Solution: The truncation error for the trapezoidal rule is, by Equation 4.4.17,

$$E_n = -\tfrac{1}{12}h^2(x_n - x_0)f''(\delta)$$

for some δ in the range $x_0 < \delta < x_n$. Five-place accuracy requires that

$$|E_n| \leq \tfrac{1}{2} \times 10^{-5}.$$

Since $f(x) = e^{-x}$ and $f''(x) = e^{-x}$, then $|f''(x)| \leq 1$ on the range $0 \leq x \leq 1$. Thus, the requirement is that

$$|E_n| \leq \tfrac{1}{12}h^2 \leq \tfrac{1}{2} \times 10^{-5}$$

or

$$h^2 \leq 6 \times 10^{-5}.$$

This last inequality is satisfied by $h = 7.745 \times 10^{-3}$. (Notice that $\sqrt{60} = 7.745967+$. The natural inclination in solving $h^2 \leq 6 \times 10^{-5}$ might be to let $h = 7.746 \times 10^{-3}$. However, with the latter value for h, $h^2 > 6 \times 10^{-5}$.) Since $n = 1/h$, h must be adjusted so that $1/h$ becomes an integer. Thus, one selection might be $h = 6.25 \times 10^{-3}$ so that $n = 160$. With such h and n, $h^2 < 6 \times 10^{-5}$ and the truncation error is less than or equal to $\tfrac{1}{2} \times 10^{-5}$.

Exercises

1. Derive Equations 4.5.8 and 4.5.9.
2. Derive Equations 4.5.10 and 4.5.11.
3. Derive Equations 4.5.12 and 4.5.13.

Problems

4.1   Derive the Gregory-Newton polynomial for four points (without the error term).

4.2   Find the error term for the four-point formula of Problem 4.1.

4.3   Evaluate the integral

$$I = \int_0^{0.1} e^x \, dx$$

by the trapezoidal rule (Equation 4.2.4) and by Simpson's one-third rule (Equation 4.5.3).

4.4   Repeat Problem 4.3, using Equation 4.5.8.

4.5   Repeat Problem 4.3, using Equation 4.5.10.

4.6   Apply the trapezoidal rule, Equation 4.4.17, to evaluate the integral

$$I = \int_{1.0}^{2.0} \sin x \, dx$$

for $h = 0.1$.   Give a complete error analysis.

4.7   Repeat Problem 4.6, using Simpson's one-third rule (Equation 4.5.7).

4.8   Given the integral

$$\int_1^2 \frac{dx}{x},$$

find the values of n and h to assure four decimal places of accuracy in evaluating this integral by Simpson's three-eighths rule (Equation 4.5.9). Evaluate the integral and check the accuracy.

4.9   Find the values of n and h needed to assure six decimal places of accuracy in evaluating the integral

$$I = \int_0^{\pi/2} \sin x \, dx,$$

using each of the five formulas given in this chapter—i.e., Equations 4.4.17, 4.5.7, 4.5.9, 4.5.11 and 4.5.13.

4.10   Produce, with the aid of a digital computer, a seven-place table of $\ln x$ for $x = 1$ to $x = 2$ by steps of 10^{-2}.   (Hint: use

$$\int_1^a \frac{dx}{x} = \ln a \quad \text{and} \quad \int_1^a \frac{dx}{x} + \int_a^b \frac{dx}{x} = \ln b.)$$

CHAPTER 5

Numerical Solution of Ordinary Differential Equations

THIS DISCUSSION of numerical solution of ordinary differential equations is limited to a single differential equation of the first order, $\dfrac{dy}{dx} = f(x, y)$, with the initial condition that $y = y_0$ when $x = x_0$. Methods for obtaining such a solution can be generalized to solve a set of simultaneous first-order equations of the form

$$\frac{dy_i}{dx} = f_i(x, y_1, y_2, \ldots, y_n), \qquad i = 1, 2, \ldots, n,$$

with initial conditions

$$y_i(x_0) = k_i, \qquad i = 1, 2, \ldots, n,$$

where the k_i are constants.

In addition, differential equations of higher order can be put into the form of a set of simultaneous equations of the first order by the introduction of new variables. Hence, the study of the solution of a single differential equation of first order is the basis of the theory of numerical solution of differential equations in general.

The reader should remember that a differential equation

$$\frac{dy}{dx} = f(x, y)$$

has in general many solutions. By a solution is meant a function $y = g(x)$

for which

$$\frac{dg(x)}{dx} = f(x, g(x)).$$

Whether or not a particular differential equation possesses a solution passing through a given point has been the subject of considerable mathematical investigation. Thus, there is a whole set of so-called "existence theorems" which generally give sufficient conditions for a solution of a given kind to pass through a given point. Moreover, if a solution does pass through a given point, a second problem is whether or not several solutions pass through that point. Again, there is a set of "uniqueness theorems" established to give sufficient conditions for a single solution to pass through a given point. Both existence and uniqueness conditions are briefly discussed in Appendix F.

In this chapter the differential equation $\frac{dy}{dx} = f(x, y)$ is assumed to have a unique solution passing through the point (x_0, y_0), the so-called initial condition. By a numerical solution to the initial-value problem is meant a set of points $(x_0, y_0), (x_1, y_1), \ldots, (x_n, y_n)$ where each point lies on or near to the solution curve which passes through (x_0, y_0). It is usually the case that the points fail to fall precisely on the solution curve, and since each point is used to help locate succeeding points, it may be the case that succeeding points miss the mark by even a wider margin. If a particular numerical solution method is such that the succeeding approximate solution points do not drift away from the solution curve, the method is called stable. The problem of stability has received detailed attention in recent years but is by no means a solved problem. The techniques developed in this chapter have proved trustworthy. For a discussion of their stability the reader may see Chapters 13, 14, 15 of Hamming's *Numerical Methods for Scientists and Engineers.**

5.1 General Approach to Numerical Solution

An approach to the numerical solution of a differential equation

$$\frac{dy}{dx} = f(x, y) \tag{5.1.1}$$

is to use one of several methods to find a few values of y, then use these starting values in a more efficient method to continue the solution.

The methods of solution usually used for starting the solution are of two classes. In the first of these two classes, y in Equation 5.1.1 is approximated by a truncated series in x. Taylor's method, which is discussed in

---

* Hamming, R. W., *Numerical Methods for Scientists and Engineers*, McGraw-Hill Book Company, New York, 1962.

Section 5.2, is a method of this type. The Runge-Kutta methods, discussed in later sections, are representative of the second class of starting procedures. In these methods truncated Taylor's series are approximated by linear combinations of functional values.

The main reason for using two methods, a starting method and a continuing method, is that the continuing method often offers greater stability. However, from a practical viewpoint, the advent of the digital computer has changed the picture. Using computers, it is often more expedient to select one method and use it for the complete solution, even though the method may not be the most efficient one possible.

For this reason, then, only a few of the many possible so-called starting methods are discussed in this chapter, with a very brief introduction to the methods in the "continuing" class, the Predictor-Corrector methods.

5.2 Taylor's Method

Consider the differential equation

$$\frac{dy}{dx} = f(x, y) \tag{5.2.1}$$

with the initial condition

$$y_0 = y(x_0), \tag{5.2.2}$$

where x_0 and y_0 are given constants.

If x_0 is not a singular point of the function, a Taylor's expansion of $y(x)$ about this point can be expressed as (see Appendix B)

$$y(x) = y_0 + (x - x_0)y'_0 + \frac{(x - x_0)^2 y''_0}{2!} + \frac{(x - x_0)^3 y'''_0}{3!} + \cdots, \tag{5.2.3}$$

where

$$y_0{}^i = \frac{d^i y}{dx^i}\bigg|_{x=x_0}. \tag{5.2.4}$$

Since evaluation of Equation 5.2.3 for a particular x gives one ordinate in the desired solution curve, this equation may be rewritten in a more useful form by letting

$$y_s = y(x_s) \quad \text{and} \quad x_s = x_0 + hs,$$

where h is the value of the constant increment in x. Then Equation 5.2.3 becomes

$$y_s = y(x_0 + hs) = y_0 + hs\, y'_0 + \frac{(hs)^2 y''_0}{2!} + \frac{(hs)^3 y'''_0}{3!} + \cdots. \tag{5.2.5}$$

To evaluate Equation 5.2.5 it is first necessary to find the derivatives $y'_0, y''_0, \ldots, y_0^{(r)}, \ldots$. Since, by Equation 5.2.1, $y' = f(x, y)$,

$$y'' = \frac{d}{dx} [f(x, y)] = \frac{\partial}{\partial x} f(x, y) + \frac{\partial}{\partial y} f(x, y) \frac{dy}{dx}. \qquad (5.2.6)$$

Similarly

$$y''' = \frac{d}{dx} \left[\frac{\partial}{\partial x} f(x, y) + \frac{\partial}{\partial y} f(x, y) \frac{dy}{dx} \right] = \frac{\partial^2}{\partial x^2} f(x, y) + 2 \frac{\partial^2}{\partial x \, \partial y} f(x, y) \frac{dy}{dx}$$

$$+ \frac{\partial^2}{\partial y^2} f(x, y) \left(\frac{dy}{dx} \right)^2 + \frac{\partial}{\partial y} f(x, y) \frac{d^2 y}{dx^2}. \qquad (5.2.7)$$

Obviously these general formulas become complex very rapidly. However, the general formulas are not needed in practice as is shown in the following example.

EXAMPLE 5.2.1   Using the Taylor's series method, find an expression for the solution, $y(x)$, given that

$$\frac{dy}{dx} = x^3 - y$$

and the initial condition $y = 1$ when $x = 0$. Use this expression to find values of y for $x = x_0 + h, x_0 + 2h; \ h = 0.1$.

Solution: With $x_0 = 0$ and $y_0 = 1$,

$$
\begin{array}{ll}
y^{(1)} = x^3 - y, & y_0^{(1)} = -1, \\
y^{(2)} = 3x^2 - y^{(1)}, & y_0^{(2)} = -y_0^{(1)} = +1, \\
y^{(3)} = 6x - y^{(2)}, & y_0^{(3)} = -y_0^{(2)} = -1, \\
y^{(4)} = 6 - y^{(3)}, & y_0^{(4)} = 6 - y_0^{(3)} = 7, \\
y^{(5)} = -y^{(4)}, & y_0^{(5)} = -y_0^{(4)} = -7, \\
y^{(6)} = -y^{(5)}, & y_0^{(6)} = -y_0^{(5)} = +7, \\
y^{(7)} = -y^{(6)}, & y_0^{(7)} = -y_0^{(6)} = -7.
\end{array}
$$

Making use of Equation 5.2.5 gives the series

$$y = 1 - x + \frac{x^2}{2} - \frac{x^3}{3!} + \frac{7x^4}{4!} - \frac{7x^5}{5!} + \frac{7x^6}{6!} + \cdots .$$

Using this expression for $x = x_0 + 0.1$ and $x = x_0 + 0.2$ gives

$$y_1 = 1 - 0.1 + \frac{(0.1)^2}{2} - \frac{(0.1)^3}{6} + \frac{7(0.1)^4}{24} + \cdots \approx 0.9048625,$$

$$y_2 = 1 - 0.2 + \frac{(0.2)^2}{2} - \frac{(0.2)^3}{6} + \frac{7(0.2)^4}{24} + \cdots \approx 0.8191333.$$

Example 5.2.1 seems to indicate that use of Taylor's method gives rise to a series in x which is not too difficult to obtain and which should be relatively easy to use.

One disadvantage to the method is the obvious one of finding the derivatives. In terms of automatic computer use, this in itself can be a very real difficulty since it may mean considerable auxiliary computation before the problem can be turned over to the computer.

An even greater disadvantage, however, comes to light under examination of the remainder term. As the range of x increases, it is necessary to include more and more terms in the series of Equation 5.2.3 in order to obtain any desired accuracy. Thus, for practical purposes, the range of x for the Taylor's expansion of Equation 5.2.3 is definitely restricted. The alternative to more terms in the expansion is to use a new x_0 and the corresponding y as computed by use of Equation 5.2.3 and then compute a new polynomial. Thus the labor of evaluating derivatives is compounded.

It is true, of course, that once the derivatives are found, in analytic form, computations for new initial conditions become simply substitution into formulas. But even this substitution into formulas is a formidable task, whether done by means of hand calculations or by computer, where each new problem requires a program for each of a number of derivatives. It seems likely then that Taylor's method for solving differential equations is of more value as a theoretical base than as a computing device.

EXAMPLE 5.2.2   Examine the solution in Example 5.2.1 for the range of x over which this solution will give y correct to four places.

Solution: The solution in Example 5.2.1 was

$$y = 1 - x + \frac{x^2}{2} - \frac{x^3}{6} + \frac{7x^4}{24} - \frac{7x^5}{120} + \frac{7x^6}{720} + \cdots .$$

This is an alternating series; hence the error resulting from truncation will be less than the first term omitted. If, then, the series is terminated with the term involving x^6, to assure four-place accuracy on y it is necessary that the remainder, R, be less than $\frac{1}{2} \times 10^{-4}$. Since $|R| \leq \left| \frac{7x^7}{7!} \right|$, it is sufficient that

$$\left| \frac{7x^7}{7!} \right| < 0.00005,$$

which gives $|x| < 0.624$; i.e., this solution carried through the term involving x^6 can be expected to give four-place accuracy only in the range of $x : |x| \leq 0.624$.

If the series is terminated with x^8,

$$\left| \frac{7x^9}{9!} \right| < 0.00005$$

and the range on x is $|x| \leq 1.112$.

It should be noted that in the preceding example the appearance of an alternating series resulted in very simple and precise truncation error analysis which is not possible in general. The general truncation error analysis involves the remainder term for Taylor's series; namely

$$\frac{y^{(r+1)}(\alpha)}{(r+1)!} (x - x_0)^{r+1},$$

where α is between x_0 and the value of x for which y is being evaluated. Since $y(x)$ is not known, it is usually difficult to obtain a reliable estimate of this truncation error term.

Exercises

1. Obtain the general solution of

$$\frac{dy}{dx} = x^2$$

by expanding y in a Taylor's series about x_0.

2. Let (x_1, y_1) lie on the solution curve which passes through (x_0, y_0) and which satisfies $\frac{dy}{dx} = f(x, y)$. If y_1 is approximated by

$$\hat{y}_1 = y_0 + (x_1 - x_0)y'_0,$$

let $y_1 - \hat{y}_1 = \epsilon$. If $\hat{y}'_1 = f(x_1, \hat{y}_1)$ and $y'_1 = f(x_1, y_1)$, use the Theorem of the Mean to find $y'_1 - \hat{y}'_1$ in terms of ϵ.

3. Continuing the above Exercise, if

$$\hat{y}_2 = \hat{y}_1 + (x_2 - x_1)\hat{y}_1,$$

find the difference $y_2 - \hat{y}_2$.

5.3 A Runge-Kutta Method

The methods, associated with the names of Runge, Kutta, and others, for forming numerical solutions of the initial-value problem

$$y' = f(x, y), \quad \text{where} \quad y(x_0) = y_0, \tag{5.3.1}$$

involve essentially replacing a truncated Taylor's series expansion in terms of derivatives by an approximation in terms of the function $f(x, y)$ only. Consider the Taylor's series of Equation 5.2.5 with x_0 replaced by x_n and with $s = 1$. Then

$$y_{n+1} = y(x_n + h) = y_n + hy'_n + \frac{h^2}{2} y''_n + \frac{h^3}{3!} y'''_n + \cdots. \tag{5.3.2}$$

In the Runge-Kutta methods, this series is to be replaced by an approximation of the form

$$y_{n+1} \approx y_n + h[\alpha_0 f(x_n, y_n) + \alpha_1 f(x_n + \mu_1 h, y_n + \lambda_1 h)$$
$$+ \alpha_2 f(x_n + \mu_2 h, y_n + \lambda_2 h) + \cdots$$
$$+ \alpha_p f(x_n + \mu_p h, y_n + \lambda_p h)]. \tag{5.3.3}$$

The problem, then, is to determine the α's, μ's and λ's so that if Equation 5.3.3 is expanded in powers of h, the coefficients of powers of h in a certain number of the leading terms in this expansion and in Equation 5.3.2 will agree.

To simplify the derivation, let $p = 1$ and let Equation 5.3.3 be expressed in the form

$$y_{n+1} \approx y_n + \alpha_0 k_0 + \alpha_1 k_1, \tag{5.3.4}$$

where

$$k_0 = hf(x_n, y_n), \tag{5.3.5}$$

$$k_1 = hf(x_n + \mu h, y_n + \lambda k_0). \tag{5.3.6}$$

The problem now is to expand k_0 and k_1 of Equation 5.3.4 in powers of h. To this end, use Taylor's series expansion in two variables on Equation 5.3.6 to obtain

$$k_1 = h[f + (\mu h f_x + \lambda k_0 f_y) + \tfrac{1}{2}(\mu^2 h^2 f_{xx} + 2\mu\lambda h k_0 f_{xy}$$
$$+ \lambda^2 k_0^2 f_{yy}) + O(h^3)], \quad (5.3.7)$$

where the abbreviated notations are defined by

$$f = f(x_n, y_n),$$

$$f_x = \left. \frac{\partial}{\partial x} f(x, y) \right|_{\substack{x=x_n \\ y=y_n}}, \qquad f_{xx} = \left. \frac{\partial^2}{\partial x^2} f(x, y) \right|_{\substack{x=x_n \\ y=y_n}}, \tag{5.3.8}$$

and $O(h^n)$ is a power series in h in which the least power of h is the nth.

Substitution of Equation 5.3.5 into Equation 5.3.7 gives

$$k_1 = hf + h^2(\mu f_x + \lambda f f_y) + \frac{h^3}{2}(\mu^2 f_{xx} + 2\mu\lambda f f_{xy} + \lambda^2 f^2 f_{yy}) + O(h^4).$$
$$\tag{5.3.9}$$

Substituting this expression for k_1 into Equation 5.3.4 gives the equation

$$y_{n+1} \approx y_n + h(\alpha_0 + \alpha_1)f + h^2 \alpha_1(\mu f_x + \lambda f f_y)$$
$$+ \frac{h^3}{2} \alpha_1(\mu^2 f_{xx} + 2\mu\lambda f f_{xy} + \lambda^2 f^2 f_{yy}) + O(h^4). \tag{5.3.10}$$

In order to compare coefficients of powers of h in Equation 5.3.10 and the Taylor's series of Equation 5.3.2, it is first necessary to express Equation 5.3.2 in the same notation as that used in Equation 5.3.10. Thus, using the definitions of Equation 5.3.8,

$$y'_n = f(x_n, y_n) = f,$$

$$y''_n = \frac{d}{dx} f(x, y) \bigg|_{\substack{x=x_n \\ y=y_n}} = f_x + f f_y,$$

$$y'''_n = \frac{d}{dx} (f_x + f f_y) \bigg|_{\substack{x=x_n \\ y=y_n}} = f_{xx} + 2 f f_{xy} + f^2 f_{yy} + f_y f_x + f f_y^2.$$

(5.3.11)

Equation 5.3.2 can be rewritten as

$$y_{n+1} = y_n + hf + \frac{h^2}{2} (f_x + f f_y)$$

$$+ \frac{h^3}{6} [f_{xx} + 2 f f_{xy} + f^2 f_{yy} + f_x f_y + f f_y^2] + O(h^4).$$

(5.3.12)

Equating coefficients of h and h^2 in Equations 5.3.10 and 5.3.12 gives rise to the following equations:

$$\alpha_0 + \alpha_1 = 1,$$
$$\mu \alpha_1 = \tfrac{1}{2},$$
$$\lambda \alpha_1 = \tfrac{1}{2}.$$

(5.3.13)

These three equations are satisfied if and only if

$$\alpha_0 = 1 - \alpha_1,$$

$$\mu = \frac{1}{2\alpha_1},$$

$$\lambda = \frac{1}{2\alpha_1},$$

(5.3.14)

and α_1 is an arbitrary nonzero constant. Replacing α_0, μ and λ by these values, Equation 5.3.10 then reduces to

$$y_{n+1} = y_n + hf + \frac{h^2}{2} (f_x + f f_y) + \frac{h^3}{8\alpha} (f_{xx} + 2 f f_{xy} + f^2 f_{yy}) + O(h^4),$$

(5.3.15)

where α_1 is replaced by α.

A comparison of the coefficients of powers of h in Equations 5.3.15 and 5.3.12, i.e., in the Runge-Kutta and Taylor expansions, shows that the two expansions do, in fact, agree through the h^2 terms. Moreover,

y_{n+1} as given by Equation 5.3.15 differs from y_{n+1} as given by Equation 5.3.12 by the truncation error:

$$T_n = h^3 \left[\frac{1}{6} - \frac{1}{8\alpha} \right] [f_{xx} + 2ff_{xy} + f^2 f_{yy} + f_y(f_x + ff_y)]$$

$$+ \frac{h^3}{8\alpha} f_y(f_x + ff_y) + O(h^4), \tag{5.3.16}$$

$$T_n = h^3 \left[\frac{1}{6} - \frac{1}{8\alpha} \right] y'''_n + \frac{h^3}{8\alpha} f_y y''_n + O(h^4). \tag{5.3.17}$$

Hence, this particular Runge-Kutta method involves a truncation error of the order h^3.

The parameter α in Equation 5.3.15 is arbitrary. Experience has indicated that $\alpha = \frac{1}{2}$ is a convenient choice. With this choice of α, $\alpha_1 = \alpha_0 = \frac{1}{2}$, $\mu = \lambda = 1$, and Equations 5.3.4 and 5.3.7 can be written as

$$y_{n+1} = y_n + \frac{1}{2}(k_0 + k_1), \tag{5.3.18}$$

where

$$k_0 = hf(x_n, y_n) \tag{5.3.19}$$

and

$$k_1 = hf(x_n + h, y_n + k_0), \tag{5.3.20}$$

or

$$y_{n+1} = y_n + \frac{h}{2}f(x_n, y_n) + \frac{h}{2}f[x_n + h, y_n + hf(x_n, y_n)]. \tag{5.3.21}$$

EXAMPLE 5.3.1   Use the Runge-Kutta method of Equation 5.3.21 to find the first two values in the approximate solution to the equation of Example 5.2.1, that is, $\dfrac{dy}{dx} = x^3 - y$ with initial condition $y_0 = 1$ for $x_0 = 0$; $h = \frac{1}{10}$.

Solution: Equation 5.3.21 for this differential equation is

$$y_{n+1} = y_n + \frac{h}{2}(x_n^3 - y_n) + \frac{h}{2}\{(x_n + h)^3 - [y_n + h(x_n^3 - y_n)]\}.$$

Then

$$y_1 = y_0 + \tfrac{1}{20}(x_0^3 - y_0) + \tfrac{1}{20}\{(x_0 + \tfrac{1}{10})^3 - [y_0 + \tfrac{1}{10}(x_0^3 - y_0)]\}$$

$$= 1 - \tfrac{1}{20} + \tfrac{1}{20}[(\tfrac{1}{10})^3 - (1 - \tfrac{1}{10})] = 0.90505,$$

$$y_2 = y_1 + \tfrac{1}{20}((x_1)^3 - y_1) + \tfrac{1}{20}\{(x_1 + \tfrac{1}{10})^3 - [y_1 + \tfrac{1}{10}(x_1^3 - y_1)]\}$$

$$= 0.90505 + 0.05[(0.1)^3 - 0.90505]$$

$$+ 0.05\{(0.2)^3 - [0.90505 + 0.1(0.1)^3 - 0.090505]\}$$

$$= 0.81951525.$$

It is of interest to compare these results with the results in Example 5.2.1. If only the first three terms in the series in Example 5.2.1 are used, i.e., through the h^2 terms, the results are $y_1 = 0.905$ and $y_2 = 0.82$, i.e., essentially three-place agreement with the results by the Runge-Kutta method. Since by either method, the error term is of order of h^3, i.e., 10^{-3} for this example, the degree of accuracy of either method is probably not greater than third place.

5.4 Other Runge-Kutta Methods

The derivation of Equation 5.3.15 guaranteed that use of Equations 5.3.4 and 5.3.5, with the parameters defined by Equation 5.3.14, will yield a solution for a differential equation, $y' = f(x, y)$, which agrees with the solution obtained from the Taylor's series expansion, using the first three terms, i.e., through the h^2 term. It is certainly true that three terms of a Taylor's expansion is not usually enough to give very accurate results, and hence this particular Runge-Kutta method cannot be expected to give results with a very great degree of accuracy. This particular method is given here only because of the relative simplicity of the derivation.

If the parameter, p, in Equation 5.3.3 is increased, equations similar to Equation 5.3.15 result which agree with the Taylor's series expansion through higher powers of h. The derivations of these equations follow the same general pattern as that for Equation 5.3.15 and are not given here.

If $p = 2$ in Equation 5.3.3, and k_0, k_1 and k_2 are employed, the requirement that the equation agree with Taylor's expansion through the h^3 term imposes six conditions on the eight parameters involved. One choice of the two arbitrary parameters leads to the formula

$$y_{n+1} = y_n + \tfrac{1}{6}(k_0 + 4k_1 + k_2) + O(h^4), \tag{5.4.1}$$

where

$$\begin{aligned}
k_0 &= hf(x_n, y_n), \\
k_1 &= hf(x_n + \tfrac{1}{2}h, y_n + \tfrac{1}{2}k_0), \\
k_2 &= hf(x_n + h, y_n + 2k_1 - k_0).
\end{aligned} \tag{5.4.2}$$

A second formula of the same type, i.e., for $p = 2$ in Equation 5.3.3, is given as

$$y_{n+1} = y_n + \tfrac{1}{4}(k_0 + 3k_2) + O(h^4), \tag{5.4.3}$$

where

$$\begin{aligned}
k_0 &= hf(x_n, y_n), \\
k_1 &= hf(x_n + \tfrac{1}{3}h, y_n + \tfrac{1}{3}k_0), \\
k_2 &= hf(x_n + \tfrac{2}{3}h, y_n + \tfrac{2}{3}k_1).
\end{aligned} \tag{5.4.4}$$

EXAMPLE 5.4.1   Work the problem in Example 5.3.1, using Equations 5.4.1 and 5.4.2. Repeat, using Equations 5.4.3 and 5.4.4.

Solution: Since $f(x, y) = x^3 - y$ and $h = 0.1$, Equations 5.4.1 and 5.4.2 are evaluated, for $n = 0$ and 1, as

$$y_1 = y_0 + \tfrac{1}{6}(k_0 + 4k_1 + k_2) + O(h^4)$$

and

$$k_0 = 0.1(x_0{}^3 - y) = -0.1,$$

$$k_1 = 0.1\left[\left(x_0 + \frac{0.1}{2}\right)^3 - \left(y_0 - \frac{0.1}{2}\right)\right] = 0.1\left[\frac{0.001}{8} - (1 - 0.05)\right]$$

$$= 0.1[0.000125 - 0.95] = -0.0949875,$$

$$k_2 = 0.1\{(x_0 + 0.1)^3 - [y_0 + 2(-0.0949875) - (-0.1)]\}$$

$$= 0.1[0.001 - (1 - 0.1899750 + 0.1)] = -0.0909025,$$

$$y_1 = 1 + \tfrac{1}{6}[-0.1 + 4(-0.0949875) - 0.0909025]$$

$$= 0.9048579.$$

For $n = 1, x_n = x_1 = 0.1, y_n = y_1 = 0.9048579,$

$$y_2 = y_1 + \tfrac{1}{6}(k_0 + 4k_1 + k_2) + O(h^4).$$

where

$$k_0 = 0.1[(0.1)^3 - 0.9048579] = -0.0903858,$$

$$k_1 = 0.1[(0.1 + 0.05)^3 - (0.9048579 - 0.0451929)] = -0.0856290,$$

$$k_2 = 0.1[(0.1 + 0.1)^3 - (0.9048579 - 0.1712580 + 0.0903858)]$$

$$= -0.0815986.$$

Then

$$y_2 = 0.9048579 + \tfrac{1}{6}[-0.0903858 - 0.3425160 - 0.0815986],$$

$$= 0.8191078.$$

For the formulas of Equations 5.4.3 and 5.4.4,

$$y_1 = y_0 + \tfrac{1}{4}(k_0 + 3k_2) + O(h^4),$$

where

$$k_0 = 0.1(0 - 1) = -0.1,$$

$$k_1 = 0.1\left[\left(0 + \frac{0.1}{3}\right)^3 - \left(1 - \frac{0.1}{3}\right)\right] = 0.1[0.0000370 - 0.9666667]$$

$$= -0.0966630,$$

$$k_2 = 0.1\left[\left(0 + \frac{0.2}{3}\right)^3 - \left(1 - \frac{2 \times 0.0966630}{3}\right)\right]$$

$$= 0.1[0.0002963 - 0.9355580]$$

$$= -0.0935262,$$

$$y_1 = 1 + \tfrac{1}{4}(-0.1 - 0.2805785) = 0.9048554.$$

Similarly

$$y_2 = y_1 + \tfrac{1}{4}(k_0 + 3k_2) + O(h^4),$$

where

$$k_0 = 0.1[(0.1)^3 - 0.9048554] = -0.0903855,$$

$$k_1 = 0.1\left[\left(0.1 + \frac{0.1}{3}\right)^3 - \left(0.9048554 - \frac{0.0903855}{3}\right)\right]$$

$$= 0.1[0.0023704 - 0.8747271] = -0.0872357,$$

$$k_2 = 0.1\left[\left(0.1 + \frac{0.2}{3}\right)^3 - (0.9048554 - 0.0581571)\right]$$

$$= 0.1[0.0046296 - 0.4866983] = -0.0842069,$$

$$y_2 = 0.9048554 + \tfrac{1}{4}[-0.0903855 - 0.2526207]$$

$$= 0.8191038.$$

By a process similar to that used in deriving Equations 5.3.18, 5.3.19, and 5.3.20, it is also possible to derive formulas for $p = 3$. The simplest such formula is of the form

$$y_{n+1} = y_n + \tfrac{1}{6}(k_0 + 2k_1 + 2k_2 + k_3) + O(h^5), \qquad (5.4.5)$$

where

$$\begin{aligned}
k_0 &= hf(x_n, y_n), \\
k_1 &= hf(x_n + \tfrac{1}{2}h, y_n + \tfrac{1}{2}k_0), \\
k_2 &= hf(x_n + \tfrac{1}{2}h, y_n + \tfrac{1}{2}k_1), \\
k_3 &= hf(x_n + h, y_n + k_2).
\end{aligned} \qquad (5.4.6)$$

Equation 5.4.5 is the one which is most commonly used on a computer to solve a differential equation.

EXAMPLE 5.4.2   Work the problem of Example 5.4.1, using Equations 5.4.5 and 5.4.6.

Solution: For this example, $f(x, y) = x^3 - y$, $x_0 = 0$, $y_0 = 1$ and $h = 0.1$. Equations 5.4.6 for x_0 and y_0 evaluate to

$$k_0 = 0.1[0 - 1] = -0.1,$$

$$k_1 = 0.1\left[(0 + 0.05)^3 - \left(1 - \frac{0.1}{2}\right)\right] = -0.0949875,$$

$$k_2 = 0.1\left[(0 + 0.05)^3 - \left(1 - \frac{0.0949875}{2}\right)\right] = -0.0952381,$$

$$k_3 = 0.1[(0 + 0.1)^3 - (1 - 0.0952381)] = -0.0903762.$$

Substitution of these values in Equation 5.4.5 gives

$$y_1 = 1 + \tfrac{1}{6}[-0.1 - 2(0.0949875) - 2(0.0952381) - 0.0903762]$$
$$= 0.9048621.$$

For y_2, Equation 5.4.5 is

$$y_2 = y_1 + \tfrac{1}{6}(k_0 + 2k_1 + 2k_2 + k_3),$$

where

$$k_0 = 0.1[(0.1)^3 - 0.904862] = -0.0903862,$$
$$k_1 = 0.1[(0.1 + 0.05)^3 - (0.9048621 - 0.0451931)]$$
$$= -0.0856294,$$
$$k_2 = 0.1[(0.1 + 0.05)^3 - (0.9048621 - 0.0428147)]$$
$$= -0.0858672,$$
$$k_3 = 0.1[(0.1 + 0.1)^3 - (0.9048621 - 0.0858672)]$$
$$= -0.0810995.$$

Then

$$y_2 = 0.9048621$$
$$+ \tfrac{1}{6}[-0.0903862 - 0.1712586 - 0.1717344 - 0.0810995]$$
$$= 0.8191156.$$

Exercise

Continue the solution of Example 5.4.2 to y_3.

5.5 Computational Advantages of the Runge-Kutta Type Methods

One rather evident advantage of the Runge-Kutta type methods over Taylor's expansion, for example, is that all calculations are in terms of the original $f(x, y)$ rather than in terms of derivatives. In terms of a digital-computer solution, this means a program for evaluation of one function rather than of one for each derivative. This statement may be somewhat misleading, since it is true that new values of the variables must be calculated at each step. The main advantage is that the formulas for these new variable values are the same for all given $f(x, y)$, whereas the derivatives required in the Taylor's series are directly dependent on the particular function. Thus once a program for any one of the Runge-Kutta methods is available, only one program to evaluate $f(x_n, y_n)$ for the particular problem is required, whereas Taylor's method would require a program for each of the derivatives used. If only one problem were to be solved and if no programs were available, the method selected would depend on the relative complexity of the two sets of formulas required. If, however, solutions to more than one problem are sought, it seems evident that a Runge-Kutta method would be more desirable from the computational standpoint.

5.6 Predictor-Corrector Method

A second approach to the solution of the differential equation

$$\frac{dy}{dx} = f(x, y) \tag{5.6.1}$$

with the initial condition $y(x_0) = y_0$ for a given value of x_0 and y_0 is widely used in computation. The methods using this approach, the predictor-corrector methods, may be arrived at as follows: If Equation 5.6.1 is integrated with respect to x between x_0 and x_i for i a positive integer, then

$$\int_{x_0}^{x_i} \frac{dy}{dt} \, dt = \int_{x_0}^{x_i} f(t, y) \, dt. \tag{5.6.2}$$

Carrying out the integration on the left side of Equation 5.6.2 gives

$$y(x_i) = y(x_0) + \int_{x_0}^{x_i} f(t, y) \, dt. \tag{5.6.3}$$

However, $y(x_0)$ is given as y_0, and the integration in Equation 5.6.3 can be approximated by a suitable quadrature formula to give

$$y(x_i) = y(x_0) + a_0 f(x_0, y(x_0)) + a_1 f(x_1, y(x_1)) + \cdots$$
$$+ a_i f(x_i, y(x_i)) + R(x_i), \tag{5.6.4}$$

where the coefficients $a_0, a_1, \ldots, a_i$ depend upon the particular quadrature formula used, and the remainder R is determined by the quadrature formula, the value of x_0, the difference $x_1 - x_0$ and the function $f(x, y)$. Since $y' = f(x, y)$, Equation 5.6.4 can be rewritten as

$$y(x_i) = y(x_0) + a_0 y'(x_0) + a_1 y'(x_1) + \cdots + a_i y'(x_i) + R(x_i). \tag{5.6.5}$$

To obtain the value of $y(x_{i+1})$ would require integration of Equation 5.6.1 again, this time between x_1 and x_{i+1} to obtain

$$y(x_{i+1}) = y(x_1) + a_0 y'(x_1) + a_1 y'(x_2) + \cdots + a_i y'(x_{i+1}) + R(x_{i+1}). \tag{5.6.6}$$

Continuing in this way, the value of y at x_{i+k}, for any positive integer k, would be obtained by

$$y(x_{i+k}) = y(x_k) + a_0 y'(x_k) + a_1 y'(x_{k+1}) + \cdots + a_i y'(x_{i+k}) + R(x_{i+k}). \tag{5.6.7}$$

A close look at Equation 5.6.7 reveals one unpleasant fact, that unless $a_i = 0$, the formula for $y(x_{i+k})$ involves $y'(x_{i+k})$. Since $y'(x_{i+k}) = f(x_{i+k}, y(x_{i+k}))$, the formula in Equation 5.6.7 cannot yield $y(x_{i+k})$. However, if an approximation to $y(x_{i+k})$ were known, then perhaps the formula for $y(x_{i+k})$ in Equation 5.6.7 could be used to improve the approximation. This, indeed, is the technique used, with the result that Equation 5.6.7 is referred to as a "corrector formula."

How then is the first approximation to $y(x_{i+k})$ to be obtained? The answer is to use the closed integration formula*

$$\int_{x_0}^{x_n} g(x)\, dx = b_0 g(x_0) + b_1 g(x_1) + \cdots + b_n g(x_n), \qquad (5.6.8)$$

in which $b_n = 0$. If such a formula is used with $n = i$ in particular, then returning to Equation 5.6.1 and integrating between x_0 and x_i gives

$$y(x_i) = y(x_0) + b_0 y'(x_0) + b_1 y'(x_1) + \cdots + b_{i-1} y'(x_{i-1}) + R(x_i),$$
$$(5.6.9)$$

where once again the coefficients $b_0, \ldots, b_{i-1}$, depend upon the particular quadrature formula and R is determined by the quadrature formula, the value of x_0, the difference $x_1 - x_0$, and the function $f(x, y)$.

In general,

$$y(x_{i+k}) = y(x_k) + b_0 y'(x_k) + \cdots + b_{i-1} y'(x_{i+k-1}) + R(x_{i+k}). \quad (5.6.10)$$

Thus an approximation to $y(x_{i+k})$ requires only a knowledge of the previous values of $y(x)$, but not $y(x_{i+k})$ itself. The formula given by Equation 5.6.10 is called a "predictor formula."

Thus, the second approach to the numerical solution of an initial-value problem can be summarized as follows: Given Equation 5.6.1 with the initial condition $y(x_0) = y_0$,

(1) Select the value of i.

(2) Obtain approximations to $y(x_1), y(x_2), \ldots, y(x_{i-1})$ by some means, probably the Runge-Kutta method.

(3) Use a predictor, Equation 5.6.10, to obtain an approximation to $y(x_i)$.

(4) Use that value of y in the right side of the corrector, Equation 5.6.7, to improve the value of $y(x_i)$.

(5) At this point one probably increases i by 1 and returns to step 3.

Predictor-corrector formulas, as with direct methods such as Runge-Kutta, make use of the previous approximate solution points to obtain

---

* See K. S. Kunz, *Numerical Analysis*, McGraw-Hill Book Company, New York, 1957, Chapter 7, in particular, Sec. 7.14.

a new solution point. As a result, errors can magnify as the solution proceeds. However, two techniques can be used in the case of the predictor-corrector method to reduce the error. First, the corrector can be used iteratively at each value of x_i to improve the approximation to $y(x_i)$. Of course it must be verified that such iterative use of the corrector produces a convergent sequence and that this sequence converges to $y(x_i)$.

An even better method for improving the approximation to $y(x_i)$ is the so-called "mop-up." The mop-up is a correction made on the approximation obtained from the corrector and is explained as follows: Let p be the predicted value of $y(x_i)$ while c is the value of $y(x_i)$ obtained by an associated corrector formula. If the predictor and corrector have been selected so that

$$p = y(x_i) + k_1 y^{(m)}(\xi), \tag{5.6.11}$$

$$c = y(x_i) + k_2 y^{(m)}(\eta), \tag{5.6.12}$$

where k_1 and k_2 are constants, m is determined by the integration formulas used, and ξ and η are values of x in the same *small* interval, then

$$p - c = k_1 y^{(m)}(\xi) - k_2 y^{(m)}(\eta). \tag{5.6.13}$$

Assuming that $\xi \approx \eta$, then

$$p - c \approx (k_1 - k_2) y^{m}(\eta) = \frac{k_1 - k_2}{k_2} k_2 y^{(m)}(\eta). \tag{5.6.14}$$

Hence

$$k_2 y^{(m)}(\eta) \approx \frac{k_2}{k_1 - k_2} (p - c); \tag{5.6.15}$$

that is, the error in the corrector is approximately $\dfrac{k_2}{k_1 - k_2} (p - c)$. Therefore the value c obtained from the corrector formula is to be corrected by adding the mop-up term

$$-\frac{k_2}{k_1 - k_2} (p - c). \tag{5.6.16}$$

Two commonly encountered predictor-corrector formulas, which for some choices, at least, of $f(x, y)$ can be stable, are developed here, namely, Milne and Adams-Bashforth methods.

5.7 Milne Methods

Milne's predictor formula is obtained by integrating Equation 5.6.1 between x_{n-3} and x_{n+1} to obtain

$$y(x_{n+1}) - y(x_{n-3}) = \int_{x_{n-3}}^{x_{n+1}} \frac{dy}{dt} \, dt = \int_{x_{n-3}}^{x_{n+1}} f(t, y) \, dt. \tag{5.7.1}$$

The particular quadrature formula selected to approximate the integral on the right side of Equation 5.7.1 is

$$\int_{x_{n-3}}^{x_{n+1}} g(t)\, dt = \frac{4}{3} h(2g(x_{n-2}) - g(x_{n-1}) + 2g(x_n)) + \frac{14}{45} h^5 g^{(4)}(\zeta), \quad (5.7.2)$$

where ζ lies between x_{n-3} and x_{n+1} and $h = x_{i+1} - x_i$.

In Equation 5.7.1, $g(t) = \dfrac{dy}{dt}$ so that Equation 5.7.1 can be written, using Equation 5.7.2, as

$$y(x_{n+1}) = y(x_{n-3}) + \frac{4h}{3}(2y'(x_{n-2}) - y'(x_{n-1}) + 2y'(x_n))$$

$$+ \frac{14}{45} h^5 y^{(5)}(\zeta), \quad (5.7.3)$$

where ζ lies between x_{n-3} and x_{n+1}.

To obtain a corrector formula, Equation 5.6.1 is integrated from x_{n-1} to x_{n+1}, with the integral evaluated by Simpson's rule, obtaining

$$y_{n+1} = y_{n-1} + \frac{h}{3}(y'(x_{n-1}) + 4y'(x_n) + y'(x_{n+1})) - \frac{h^5 y^5(\eta)}{90}, \quad (5.7.4)$$

where η lies between x_{n-1} and x_{n+1}.

EXAMPLE 5.7.1   Use Milne's predictor and corrector to obtain and improve an approximation to $y(x_4)$ of

$$\frac{dy}{dx} = x^3 - y$$

with an initial condition $x_0 = 0$, $y_0 = 1$.

Solution: From Example 5.4.2 approximations (using $h = 0.1$) to y_1 and y_2 can be obtained as follows:

$$y_1 = 0.9048621, \qquad y_2 = 0.8191158,$$

while another application of the Runge-Kutta method used in that example gives

$$y_3 = 0.7427280.$$

Using Equation 5.7.3, the predictor for y_4 is

$$y_4 = y_0 + \frac{4h}{3}(2y'_1 - y'_2 + 2y'_3) + O(h^5).$$

To obtain y'_1, y'_2, y'_3, use

$$\frac{dy}{dx} = x^3 - y$$

to arrive at

$$y'_1 = x_1{}^3 - y_1 = -0.9038621,$$

$$y'_2 = x_2{}^3 - y_2 = -0.8111158,$$

$$y'_3 = x_3{}^3 - y_3 = -0.7157280.$$

Then

$$y_4 = y_0 + \frac{0.4}{3}(-2.4280644) + O(h^5)$$

$$= 0.6762581 + O(h^5).$$

Using Equation 5.7.4, the corrector for y_4 is

$$y_4 = y_2 + \frac{h}{3}(y'_2 + 4y'_3 + y'_4) + O(h^5).$$

The values of y'_2 and y'_3 are as previously calculated, while

$$y'_4 = x_3{}^4 - y_4 = 0.064 - 0.6762581$$

or

$$y'_4 = -0.6122581.$$

Then

$$y_4 = y_2 + \frac{0.1}{3}(-4.2862859) + O(h^5) = 0.6762396.$$

Thus the corrected value of y_4 differs from the predicted value by 0.0000185.

If the values of y and y' at the various values of x in this example were all exact, then the error in the predictor would be $(14/45)h^5 y^{(5)}(\zeta)$ while in the corrector the error would be $-(1/90)h^5 y^{(5)}(\eta)$. Thus, the only difference between the value of y obtained in the two formulas would be due to the difference in truncation error, namely

$$\delta = \frac{h^5}{90}[28 y^{(5)}(\zeta) + y^{(5)}(\eta)]. \tag{5.7.5}$$

Assuming that these two derivatives do not differ greatly, this becomes

$$\delta \approx \frac{29}{90} h^5 y^{(5)}(\eta) = -29\left(\frac{-h^5 y^{(5)}(\eta)}{90}\right). \tag{5.7.6}$$

Thus the truncation error in the corrector is approximately $-(1/29)\delta$ or $-(1/29)(p - c)$, and the truncation error in the corrected value of y_4 in Example 5.7.1 is approximately -0.0000006. Hence, for the mop-up add $+0.0000006$ to the corrected value to obtain 0.6762402 as the value of y_4.

5.8   Adams-Bashforth Quadrature

The quadrature formula known as the Adams-Bashforth formula is based upon an interpolation polynomial similar to the Gregory-Newton interpolation formula. As in that formula,

$$u = \frac{x - x_0}{h}, \tag{5.8.1}$$

but the differences used are ascending differences defined by

$$\nabla f(x) = f(x) - f(x - h) \tag{5.8.2}$$

and

$$\nabla^{m+1} f(x) = \nabla(\nabla^m f(x)), \qquad m = 1, 2, 3, \ldots .$$

The polynomial passing through $m + 1$ distinct points can be written in ascending differences as

$$y = P_m(x) = y_0 + u^{\{1\}} \nabla y_0 + \frac{1}{2!} u^{\{2\}} \nabla^2 y_0 + \cdots + \frac{1}{m!} u^{\{m\}} y_0, \tag{5.8.3}$$

where

$$u^{\{m\}} = u(u + 1) \cdots (u + m - 1). \tag{5.8.4}$$

Equation 5.8.3 can be derived in a manner similar to that in which the Gregory-Newton formula was derived.

If Equation 5.8.3 is used with y replaced by y' and $m = 3$, there follows

$$y' = y'_0 + u\nabla y'_0 + \frac{u(u + 1)}{2} \nabla^2 y'_0 + \frac{u(u + 1)(u + 2)}{6} \nabla^3 y'_0 + O(h^4). \tag{5.8.5}$$

Next, integrate both sides of Equation 5.8.5 with respect to u between $u = 0$ and $u = 1$. On the left side, since $du = \dfrac{dx}{h}$,

$$\int_0^1 y' \, du = \frac{1}{h} \int_{x_0}^{x_1} y' \, dx = \frac{1}{h}(y_1 - y_0). \tag{5.8.6}$$

Upon integrating the right side of Equation 5.8.5, there results

$$y_1 = y_0 + h(y'_0 + \tfrac{1}{2}\nabla y'_0 + \tfrac{5}{12}\nabla^2 y'_0 + \tfrac{3}{8}\nabla^3 y'_0) + O(h^5). \tag{5.8.7}$$

Replacing y_1 by y_{n+1} and y_0 by y_n, and making use of the definitions in Equation 5.8.2, the formula in Equation 5.8.7 reduces to

$$y_{n+1} = y_n + \frac{h}{24}(55y'_n - 59y'_{n-1} + 37y'_{n-2} - 9y'_{n-3}) + O(h^5). \tag{5.8.8}$$

The precise form of the remainder is

$$\frac{251}{6} \frac{h^5 y^{(5)}(\zeta)}{5!}. \tag{5.8.9}$$

This formula is used as a predictor, with no corrector generally used. However, the Milne corrector, which can be stable for certain functions $f(x, y)$, may be used.

The major difference between the Adams-Bashforth predictor and Milne's is that the former makes use of one more derivative term. Moreover, the formula is stable in certain cases where Milne's formula is not.

Exercises

1. For the problem in Example 5.7.1 approximate y_4 by the Adams-Bashforth method, corrected by Milne's corrector.

2. Derive Equation 5.8.8 from Equation 5.8.7.

3. Derive the remainder in Equation 5.8.9.

5.9 Differential Equations of Higher than First Order

It was pointed out in the introduction to this chapter that a method for obtaining a solution for a first-order differential equation can be generalized to solve a set of simultaneous first-order equations and that a higher-order ordinary differential equation can be reduced to a system of first-order differential equations.

A method for reducing a higher-order differential equation to a system of first-order differential equations is as follows. Let the differential equation be

$$f(x, y, y', y'', \ldots, y^{(n)}) = 0. \tag{5.9.1}$$

Analogous to the initial condition imposed in Equation 5.2.2, there is imposed, in this case, the condition that the solution $y = y(x)$ of Equation 5.9.1 must satisfy

$$y(x_0) = y_0,$$
$$y'(x_0) = y'_0,$$
$$\cdot$$
$$\cdot \tag{5.9.2}$$
$$\cdot$$
$$y^{(n-1)}(x_0) = y_0^{(n-1)},$$

where $y_0, y'_0, \ldots, y_0^{(n-1)}$ are constants. To reduce Equation 5.9.1 to a system of first-order equations, make the substitutions

$$y' = z_1,$$
$$y'' = z_2,$$
$$\vdots$$
$$y^{(n-1)} = z_{n-1},$$

(5.9.3)

where the z_i are functions of x, y and the derivatives of y. Then Equation 5.9.1 is equivalent to the system of n equations

$$y' = z_1,$$
$$z'_1 = z_2,$$
$$z'_2 = z_3,$$
$$\vdots$$
$$z'_{n-2} = z_{n-1},$$
$$f(x, y, z_1, z_2, \ldots, z_{n-1}, z'_{n-1}) = 0.$$

(5.9.4)

Moreover, the initial conditions for the Equations 5.9.4 are, from Equation 5.9.2,

$$y(x_0) = y_0,$$
$$z_1(x_0) = y'_0,$$
$$\vdots$$
$$z_{n-1}(x_0) = y_0^{(n-1)}.$$

EXAMPLE 5.9.1   Reduce the equation

$$y''' + 4xy'' - y' + y = \sin x$$

to a system of first-order equations. The initial conditions are $y(0) = y'(0) = 0$, $y''(0) = 1$.

Solution: Let

$$y' = z_1, \quad\quad y'' = z_2.$$

Then the third-order equation above is equivalent to the system

$$y' = z_1,$$
$$z'_1 = z_2,$$
$$z'_2 = -4xz_2 + z_1 - y + \sin x.$$

The initial conditions become

$$y(0) = z_1(0) = 0, \qquad z_2(0) = 1.$$

In view of the fact that a higher-order differential equation can be reduced to a system of first-order equations, the next section is devoted to the numerical solution of a system of first-order equations.

Exercise

Consider the equation

$$y^{(n)} + a_{n-1}y^{(n-1)} + \cdots + a_1 y' + a_0 y = 0,$$

where the coefficients $a_0, a_1, \ldots, a_{n-1}$ are constants. Show that this equation is equivalent to the matrix equation

$$\frac{d\mathscr{Z}}{dt} = \mathscr{A}\mathscr{Z},$$

where

$$\mathscr{Z} = \begin{bmatrix} y \\ z_1 \\ z_2 \\ \vdots \\ z_{n-1} \end{bmatrix}$$

and

$$\mathscr{A} = \begin{bmatrix} 0 & 1 & 0 & 0 & \cdots & 0 \\ 0 & 0 & 1 & 0 & \cdots & 0 \\ \vdots & & & & & \vdots \\ 0 & 0 & 0 & 0 & \cdots & 1 \\ -a_0 & -a_1 & -a_2 & -a_3 & \cdots & -a_{n-1} \end{bmatrix}.$$

5.10 Numerical Solution of Systems of First-Order Equations by the Runge–Kutta Method

The numerical solution of a system of equations is illustrated in this section. The Runge-Kutta method used in the illustration is the fourth-order method given in Equation 5.4.5 since that formula is the most commonly used Runge-Kutta formula.

Let it be required, for example, to produce a numerical solution for the system of equations

$$y' = p(x, y, z, w), \qquad z' = q(x, y, z, w), \qquad w' = r(x, y, z, w), \qquad (5.10.1)$$

with the initial condition
$$y(x_0) = y_0,$$
$$z(x_0) = z_0, \qquad (5.10.2)$$
$$w(x_0) = w_0.$$

Equation 5.4.5 is replaced in this case by
$$y_{n+1} = y_n + \tfrac{1}{6}(k_0 + 2k_1 + 2k_2 + k_3),$$
$$z_{n+1} = z_n + \tfrac{1}{6}(l_0 + 2l_1 + 2l_2 + l_3), \qquad (5.10.3)$$
$$w_{n+1} = w_n + \tfrac{1}{6}(m_0 + 2m_1 + 2m_2 + m_3),$$

where the k_i, l_i, and m_i are specified, in the order of computation by

Step 1
$$k_0 = hp(x_n, y_n, z_n, w_n),$$
$$l_0 = hq(x_n, y_n, z_n, w_n), \qquad (5.10.4)$$
$$m_0 = hr(x_n, y_n, z_n, w_n);$$

Step 2
$$k_1 = hp\left(x_n + \frac{h}{2}, y_n + \frac{k_0}{2}, z_n + \frac{l_0}{2}, w_n + \frac{m_0}{2}\right),$$
$$l_1 = hq\left(x_n + \frac{h}{2}, y_n + \frac{k_0}{2}, z_n + \frac{l_0}{2}, w_n + \frac{m_0}{2}\right), \qquad (5.10.5)$$
$$m_1 = hr\left(x_n + \frac{h}{2}, y_n + \frac{k_0}{2}, z_n + \frac{l_0}{2}, w_n + \frac{m_0}{2}\right);$$

Step 3
$$k_2 = hp\left(x_n + \frac{h}{2}, y_n + \frac{k_1}{2}, z_n + \frac{l_1}{2}, w_n + \frac{m_1}{2}\right),$$
$$l_2 = hq\left(x_n + \frac{h}{2}, y_n + \frac{k_1}{2}, z_n + \frac{l_1}{2}, w_n + \frac{m_1}{2}\right), \qquad (5.10.6)$$
$$m_2 = hr\left(x_n + \frac{h}{2}, y_n + \frac{k_1}{2}, z_n + \frac{l_1}{2}, w_n + \frac{m_1}{2}\right);$$

Step 4
$$k_3 = hp(x_n + h, y_n + k_2, z_n + l_2, w_n + m_2),$$
$$l_3 = hq(x_n + h, y_n + k_2, z_n + l_2, w_n + m_2), \qquad (5.10.7)$$
$$m_3 = hr(x_n + h, y_n + k_2, z_n + l_2, w_n + m_2).$$

The method of solution then proceeds as follows:

1. Set $n = 0$.
2. Calculate the quantities in Step 1, all for the same values of the arguments.

3. Calculate the quantities of Step 2. Observe that all the quantities required in Step 2 are calculated in Step 1, or else were given previously.
4. Calculate the quantities in Step 3.
5. Calculate the quantities in Step 4.
6. Evaluate Equations 5.10.3.
7. Advance the value of n by 1.
8. Go to the second statement in this list.

EXAMPLE 5.10.1   Produce y_1 by the Runge-Kutta fourth-order method, accurate to four decimal places, for the equation

$$y''' + y'' + yy' + x^2 = 0$$

with initial conditions

$$y(0) = y'(0) = y''(0) = 0.$$

Solution: First, reduce the equation as in Section 5.9 by the substitution $y' = z$ and $z' = w$ to

$$y' = z, \quad z' = w, \quad w' = -w - yz - x^2$$

with the initial conditions

$$y(0) = z(0) = w(0) = 0.$$

Since the accuracy of the Runge-Kutta fourth-order method is of the order of h^5, then select h so that

$$h^5 \leq 5 \cdot 10^{-5}$$

or

$$h \leq \sqrt[5]{5} \cdot 10^{-1}.$$

But

$$1.3 \leq \sqrt[5]{5} < 1.4.$$

Thus, select $h = 0.13 \leq \sqrt[5]{5} \cdot 10^{-1}$.

In this problem, the p, q, and r of Equations 5.10.1 are

$$p(x, y, z, w) = z, \quad q(x, y, z, w) = w, \quad r(x, y, z, w) = -w - yz - x^2.$$

Equations 5.10.4 through 5.10.7 become

Step 1

$$k_0 = 0.13z_n,$$
$$l_0 = 0.13w_n,$$
$$m_0 = -0.13(w_n + y_n z_n + x_n^2);$$

Step 2

$$k_1 = 0.13\left(z_n + \frac{l_0}{2}\right),$$

$$l_1 = 0.13\left(w_n + \frac{m_0}{2}\right),$$

$$m_1 = -0.13\left[w_n + \frac{m_0}{2} + \left(y_n + \frac{k_0}{2}\right)\left(z_n + \frac{l_0}{2}\right) + \left(x_n + \frac{0.13}{2}\right)^2\right];$$

Step 3

$$k_2 = 0.13\left(z_n + \frac{l_1}{2}\right),$$

$$l_2 = 0.13\left(w_n + \frac{m_1}{2}\right),$$

$$m_2 = -0.13\left[w_n + \frac{m_1}{2} + \left(y_n + \frac{k_1}{2}\right)\left(z_n + \frac{l_1}{2}\right) + \left(x_n + \frac{0.13}{2}\right)^2\right];$$

Step 4

$$k_3 = 0.13(z_n + l_2),$$
$$l_3 = 0.13(w_n + m_2),$$
$$m_3 = -0.13[w_n + m_2 + (y_n + k_2)(z_n + l_2) + (x_{n+1})^2].$$

Starting with $n = 0$, there follows

Step 1

$$k_0 = 0,$$
$$l_0 = 0,$$
$$m_0 = 0;$$

Step 2

$$k_1 = 0,$$
$$l_1 = 0,$$
$$m_1 = -0.13\left[\left(\frac{0.13}{2}\right)^2\right] = -0.00054925;$$

Step 3

$$k_2 = 0,$$

$$l_2 = 0.13\left(-\frac{0.00054925}{2}\right) = -0.00003570,$$

$$m_2 = -0.13\left[-\frac{0.00054925}{2} + \left(\frac{0.13}{2}\right)^2\right] = -0.00051355;$$

Step 4

$$k_3 = 0.13(-0.00003570) = -0.00000464,$$

$$l_3 = 0.13(-0.00051355) = -0.00006676,$$

$$m_3 = -0.13[-0.00051355 + (0.13)^2] = -0.00213024.$$

Then Equations 5.10.3 become

$$y_1 = \tfrac{1}{6}[-0.00000464]$$

$$= -7.7 \times 10^{-7},$$

$$y'_1 = z_1 = \tfrac{1}{6}[2(-0.00003570) + (-0.00006676)]$$

$$= -2.303 \times 10^{-5},$$

$$y''_1 = w_1 = \tfrac{1}{6}[2(-0.00054925) + 2(-0.00051355) + (-0.00213024)]$$

$$= -7.0931 \times 10^{-4}.$$

To four decimal places, $y_1 = z_1 = 0$ while $w_1 = -0.0007$.

Next, to obtain y_2, z_2, w_2, increase n by 1 and repeat the entire process.

Problems

5.1   Find the first eight terms of the Taylor's series solution to the equation

$$dy/dx = x^2 + y^2$$

with the initial condition that when $x = 0$, $y = 0$.

5.2   Repeat Problem 5.1 with the new initial condition that when $x = 10^{-1}$, $y = 10^{-1}$.

5.3   Referring to Appendix F, Theorem F.1, the Cauchy-Peano Theorem, verify that there is at least one continuous solution of $dy/dx = x^2 + y^2$ which passes through the point $(0, 0)$ and that there is at least one which passes through $(10^{-1}, 10^{-1})$.

5.4   Referring to Appendix F, Theorem F.2, verify that the solution curve in Problems 5.3 which passes through $(0, 0)$ is the only solution curve of $\dfrac{dy}{dx} = x^2 + y^2$ which passes through $(0, 0)$.

5.5   Determine a value of h which will give a truncation error of the order of $\tfrac{1}{2} \cdot 10^{-6}$ for the Runge-Kutta formula given in Equation 5.4.5, for the problem

$$\frac{dy}{dx} = -\frac{x}{y}$$

with the initial condition $x = 1$, $y = 1$.

5.6   Use Equation 5.4.5 to obtain y_1, y_2 and y_3 for Problem 5.5. Then use the Adams-Bashforth predictor and Milne's corrector to approximate y_4.

5.7   Repeat Problems 5.5 and 5.6 for the initial condition $x = 1, y = 0$.

5.8   Reduce the equation

$$xy''' - 3yy'' + y' = 4$$

with initial condition $y(0) = y'(0) = y''(0) = 1$ to a system of first-order differential equations, with appropriate initial conditions.

5.9   Use the method illustrated in Section 5.10 with $h = 10^{-1}$ to find y_1 and z_1 for the system

$$y' = x + yz,$$
$$z' = z + x$$

with the initial conditions that when $x = 1$, $y = 0$ and $z = 1$.

5.10   Generalize the Milne predictor and corrector, Equations 5.7.3 and 5.7.4, to the case in which

$$y' = f(x, y, z),$$
$$z' = g(x, y, z).$$

CHAPTER 6

Linear Algebraic Equations
and Matrices

SETS OF simultaneous linear constant coefficient algebraic equations arise in many fields of applied mathematics, for example normal equations in statistics, network equations (node or mesh) in electric network theory, and difference equations in approximating the solution of linear differential equations or an integral equation by using lattice points.

While it is theoretically possible to use the well-known direct method of determinants, in practice the number of operations required for sets of equations of large order is so great that even in high-speed computers the amount of time consumed is large enough to be prohibitive. Also the problem of round-off error for large sets is a very serious problem in a method requiring so many operations.

Most of this chapter is concerned with one basic method of both equation solution and matrix inversion.

6.1 Method of Elimination or Gauss Reduction Method

The process of eliminating one unknown at a time is perhaps the simplest and shortest method of solving a set of simultaneous equations. This method is the one most frequently used in introductory courses in Algebra but its application is usually restricted to a relatively small number of equations.

For a large set of equations, the elimination process must obviously be organized in some orderly fashion. The Gauss reduction technique is such an organization.

Consider the set of equations

$$a_{11}x_1 + a_{12}x_2 + \cdots + a_{1n}x_n = b_1,$$
$$a_{21}x_1 + a_{22}x_2 + \cdots + a_{2n}x_n = b_2,$$
$$\vdots$$
$$a_{n-1,1}x_1 + a_{n-1,2}x_2 + \cdots + a_{n-1,n}x_n = b_{n-1},$$
$$a_{n1}x_1 + a_{n2}x_2 + \cdots + a_{nn}x_n = b_n. \tag{6.1.1}$$

While the Gauss reduction technique can be considered as a method of eliminating variables, it seems much more desirable to think of it as a method for reducing the coefficient matrix to a triangular matrix. Working in terms of the coefficient matrix rather than in terms of variables has the special advantage that all the theory can be applied directly to the problem of matrix inversion without artificially introducing variables which are not actually involved in the problem.

Consider, then, the augmented matrix of coefficients and constant terms of Equation 6.1.1:

$$\mathscr{A}_a = \begin{bmatrix} a_{11} & a_{12} & \cdots & a_{1n} & b_1 \\ a_{21} & a_{22} & \cdots & a_{2n} & b_2 \\ \vdots & & & & \vdots \\ a_{n1} & a_{n2} & \cdots & a_{nn} & b_n \end{bmatrix}. \tag{6.1.2}$$

The Gauss reduction technique reduces this augmented matrix to the form

$$\mathscr{A}_{a,n-1} = \begin{bmatrix} a_{11} & a_{12} & \cdots & a_{1n} & b_1 \\ 0 & a'_{22} & \cdots & a'_{2n} & b'_2 \\ \vdots & & & & \vdots \\ 0 & 0 & \cdots & a'_{nn} & b'_n \end{bmatrix}, \tag{6.1.3}$$

where all the elements below the diagonal of the original coefficient matrix have been reduced to zeros by row operations.

The first step in the reduction is to replace the entries in the first column by zeros, except for the entry a_{11}. This is accomplished by subtracting the product of the first row and a_{k1}/a_{11} from the kth row for $k = 2, 3, \ldots, n$. The result is that a_{k1} is replaced by 0 for $k = 2, 3, \ldots, n$ while a_{ki} and b_k are replaced by

$$a'_{ki} = a_{ki} - \frac{a_{k1}}{a_{11}} a_{1i}, \qquad b'_k = b_k - \frac{a_{k1}}{a_{11}} b_1, \tag{6.1.4}$$

where $k = 2, 3, \ldots, n$ and $i = 1, 2, 3, \ldots, n$.

The operation defined in Equations 6.1.4 is equivalent to the following:

1. Form the ratio a_{21}/a_{11}.
2. Multiply row 1 by the ratio in Step 1.
3. Subtract these products from row 2, term by term.
4. Repeat for $a_{31}/a_{11}, \ldots, a_{n1}/a_{11}$ and for rows $3, 4, \ldots, n$ in Steps 2 and 3, respectively.

The matrix of Equation 6.1.2 is now reduced to

$$\mathscr{A}_{a1} = \begin{bmatrix} a_{11} & a_{12} & \cdots & a_{1n} & b_1 \\ 0 & a'_{22} & \cdots & a'_{2n} & b'_2 \\ \vdots & & & & \vdots \\ 0 & a'_{n2} & \cdots & a'_{nn} & b'_n \end{bmatrix}. \tag{6.1.5}$$

The process as defined in Equations 6.1.4 is now carried out for the submatrix formed by striking out the first row and first column of Equation 6.1.5. The formulas of Equation 6.1.4 become

$$a''_{ki} = a'_{ki} - \frac{a'_{k2}}{a'_{22}} a'_{2i}, \quad b''_k = b'_k - \frac{a'_{k2}}{a'_{22}} b'_2, \tag{6.1.6}$$

where

$$k = 3, 4, \ldots, n$$

and

$$i = 2, 3, \ldots, n.$$

This process is repeated until all terms below the main diagonal are zero, i.e. until the matrix of Equation 6.1.3 is generated.

The set of equations for which Equation 6.1.3 is the augmented coefficient matrix is

$$\begin{bmatrix} a_{11} & a_{12} & \cdots & a_{1n} \\ 0 & a'_{22} & \cdots & a'_{2n} \\ \vdots & & & \vdots \\ 0 & 0 & \cdots & a'_{nn} \end{bmatrix} \begin{bmatrix} x_1 \\ x_2 \\ \vdots \\ x_n \end{bmatrix} = \begin{bmatrix} b_1 \\ b'_2 \\ \vdots \\ b'_n \end{bmatrix}. \tag{6.1.7}$$

The next step can be viewed as a "back substitution" process or as a process of obtaining the matrix equation

$$\begin{bmatrix} 1 & 0 & \cdots & 0 \\ 0 & 1 & \cdots & 0 \\ \vdots & & & \vdots \\ 0 & 0 & \cdots & 1 \end{bmatrix} \begin{bmatrix} x_1 \\ x_2 \\ \vdots \\ x_n \end{bmatrix} = \begin{bmatrix} b'_1 \\ b''_2 \\ \vdots \\ b''_n \end{bmatrix}. \tag{6.1.8}$$

In actual practice, the steps involved in generating the unit matrix on the left of Equation 6.1.8 are of importance only as they reflect into the formation of the solution vector, $\mathscr{B}$. The "back substitution" formulas are exactly those that describe this reflection into the solution vector $\mathscr{B}$; hence the "back substitution" approach is given here.

The last equation obtained by performing the indicated multiplication of Equation 6.1.7 is an equation in one unknown. If now x_n is determined by

$$x_n = \frac{b'_n}{a'_{nn}}, \tag{6.1.9}$$

and this value is substituted into the next to the last equation in the set, this equation becomes also an equation in one unknown, which can be solved as

$$x_{n-1} = \frac{b'_{n-1} - a'_{n-1,\,n}x_n}{a'_{n-1,n-1}}. \tag{6.1.10}$$

In general

$$x_k = \frac{b'_k - a'_{kn}x_n - a'_{k,n-1}x_{n-1} - \cdots - a'_{k,k+1}x_{k+1}}{a'_{kk}}, \tag{6.1.11}$$

where

$$k = n - 1, n - 2, \ldots, 3, 2, 1.$$

EXAMPLE 6.1.1   Use the Gauss reduction technique to solve the set of equations

$$
\begin{aligned}
6x_1 - x_2 - 3x_3 &= 100, \\
-x_1 + 4x_2 &= -50, \\
-3x_1 + 5x_3 &= 75.
\end{aligned}
$$

Carry all results out to 4 decimal places.

Solution: The original augmented matrix for this set of equations is

$$\mathscr{A}_a = \begin{bmatrix} 6 & -1 & -3 & 100 \\ -1 & 4 & 0 & -50 \\ -3 & 0 & 5 & 75 \end{bmatrix}.$$

For this matrix, $\dfrac{a_{21}}{a_{11}} = -\dfrac{1}{6}$. Then

$$a'_{22} = 4 - (-1)(-\tfrac{1}{6}) = 3.8333,$$
$$a'_{23} = 0 - (-3)(-\tfrac{1}{6}) = -0.5000,$$
$$b'_2 = -50 - (100)(-\tfrac{1}{6}) = -33.3333.$$

Likewise $\dfrac{a_{31}}{a_{11}} = -\dfrac{3}{6} = -\dfrac{1}{2}$, so that

$$a'_{32} = 0 - (-1)(-\tfrac{1}{2}) = -0.5000,$$
$$a'_{33} = 5 - (-3)(-\tfrac{1}{2}) = 3.5000,$$
$$b'_3 = 75 - (100)(-\tfrac{1}{2}) = 125.0000.$$

The augmented matrix is now reduced to

$$\mathscr{A}_{a1} = \begin{bmatrix} 6 & -1 & -3 & 100 \\ 0 & 3.8333 & -0.5 & -33.3333 \\ 0 & -0.5 & 3.5 & 125 \end{bmatrix}.$$

Operating on the second column of $\mathscr{A}_{a1}$:

$$\frac{a'_{32}}{a'_{22}} = \frac{-0.5}{3.833} = -0.1304,$$
$$a''_{33} = 3.5 - (-0.5)(-0.1304) = 3.4348,$$
$$b''_3 = 125 - (-33.3333)(-0.1304) = 120.6533.$$

Equation 6.1.7 for this problem is then

$$\begin{bmatrix} 6 & -1 & -3 \\ 0 & 3.8333 & -0.5 \\ 0 & 0 & 3.4348 \end{bmatrix}\begin{bmatrix} x_1 \\ x_2 \\ x_3 \end{bmatrix} = \begin{bmatrix} 100 \\ -33.3333 \\ 120.6533 \end{bmatrix}.$$

By "back substitution,"

$$x_3 = \frac{120.6533}{3.4348} = 35.1267,$$
$$x_2 = \frac{-33.3333 - (-0.5)(35.1267)}{3.8333} = -4.1139,$$
$$x_1 = \frac{100 - (-3)(35.1267) - (-1)(-4.1139)}{6} = 33.5444.$$

One of the drawbacks of the Gauss reduction method is that errors are accumulative and the values of the variables are apt to be successively more inaccurate as the back-substitution process continues. For if referring to Equation 6.1.11, the error in the numerator is ϵ, say, the error in x_k is approximately $\dfrac{\epsilon}{a'_{kk}}$. If $|a'_{kk}| < 1$, the magnitude of the error in x_k exceeds $|\epsilon|$, whereas if $|a'_{kk}| > 1$, the magnitude of the error in x_k is less than $|\epsilon|$. This leads to the conclusion that it is desirable to make each diagonal element in the triangular matrix as large as possible.

Since a relatively large diagonal term is desirable, a technique of row interchanging is often used. In this technique, the so-called pivotal technique, before the below-diagonal elements in a particular column, say the jth, are reduced to zero, the elements in that column are examined. If any element in the column is such that

$$|a_{ij}| > |a_{jj}|, \qquad j < i \leq n,$$

an interchange of rows i and j is made. Since this is equivalent to a reordering of the equations only, the order of the variables and hence the order of the results is unchanged by this row interchange.

Exercises

1. Show by the Gauss reduction technique that the matrix

$$\mathscr{A} = \begin{bmatrix} 1 & 2 & 3 \\ 2 & 4 & 5 \\ 3 & 6 & 7 \end{bmatrix}$$

is singular.

2. Is the system

$$x + 2y + 3z = -5,$$
$$2x + 4y + 5z = -10,$$
$$3x + 6y + 7z = -15$$

solvable for x, y, and z? If so, find all solutions.

6.2 Variations on the Gauss Reduction Method

There are several variations of the Gauss reduction method. These methods are mainly tabulation techniques for organizing the computations, designed to introduce a particular ordering to take advantage of certain properties of desk calculators, to reduce the number of operations, and to introduce checks at various stages in the computation. If desk calculators are to be used on a number of problems, use of one of these tabular methods is certainly desirable. However, with use of a digital computer, the direct use of the reduction technique is probably more to be desired since there is considerable time and effort involved in becoming sufficiently familiar with one of the tabular methods to make use of it.

A direct extension of the Gauss reduction technique is the Gauss–Jordan Method. In this method, the elements above the diagonal are eliminated along with those below the diagonal. Thus, the elements below the diagonal in the first column are eliminated as in the Gauss method. Then, when the elements below the diagonal in the second column have been eliminated, the element above the diagonal is also eliminated. This process then is repeated for each column, with the result that the final matrix obtained is a diagonal matrix. The particular formula used in this case is

$$a'_{ij} = a_{ij} - \frac{a_{ik}}{a'_{kk}} a'_{kj}, \qquad b'_i = b_i - \frac{a_{ik}}{a'_{kk}} b_k, \qquad (6.2.1)$$

where

$$i = 1, 2, \ldots, \qquad k = 2, \ldots, n, \qquad i < k.$$

For example, to obtain zero in the first row, second-column position

$$a'_{12} = a_{12} - \frac{a_{12}}{a'_{22}} a'_{22}. \qquad (6.2.2)$$

Then also

$$a'_{13} = a_{13} - \frac{a_{12}}{a'_{22}} a'_{23},$$

$$\vdots$$

$$a'_{1n} = a_{1n} - \frac{a_{12}}{a'_{22}} a'_{2n}, \qquad (6.2.3)$$

$$b'_1 = b_1 - \frac{a_{12}}{a'_{22}} b'_2.$$

The final set of equations by this method is, in matrix form,

$$\begin{bmatrix} a'_{11} & 0 & \cdots & 0 \\ 0 & a'_{22} & \cdots & 0 \\ \cdot & & & \cdot \\ \cdot & & & \cdot \\ \cdot & & & \cdot \\ 0 & 0 & \cdots & a'_{nn} \end{bmatrix} \begin{bmatrix} x_1 \\ x_2 \\ \cdot \\ \cdot \\ \cdot \\ x_n \end{bmatrix} = \begin{bmatrix} b'_1 \\ b'_2 \\ \cdot \\ \cdot \\ \cdot \\ b'_n \end{bmatrix}, \qquad (6.2.4)$$

which is a set of equations, each in only one variable, that can be solved by simple division.

EXAMPLE 6.2.1 Solve the equations of Example 6.1.1 by the Gauss–Jordan Method.

Solution: Since a triangular matrix was obtained in Example 6.1.1, start with this triangular matrix, namely

$$\mathscr{A}_{a2} = \begin{bmatrix} 6 & -1 & -3 & 100 \\ 0 & 3.8333 & -0.5 & -33.3333 \\ 0 & 0 & 3.4348 & 120.6533 \end{bmatrix}.$$

To replace the terms above the main diagonal by zeros use the following transformations:

$$\frac{a_{12}}{a_{22}} = -\frac{1}{3.8333} = -0.2609,$$

$$a'_{13} = -3 - (-0.5)(-0.2609) = -3.1304,$$

$$b'_1 = 100 - (33.3333)(-0.2609) = 91.3043,$$

$$\frac{a'_{13}}{a_{33}} = -\frac{3.1304}{3.4348} = -0.9114,$$

$$b''_1 = 91.3043 - (120.6533)(-0.9114) = 201.2677,$$

$$\frac{a_{23}}{a_{33}} = -\frac{0.5}{3.4348} = -0.1456,$$

$$b'_2 = -33.3333 - (120.6533)(-0.1456) = -15.7662.$$

The final set of equations is now

$$\begin{bmatrix} 6 & 0 & 0 \\ 0 & 3.8333 & 0 \\ 0 & 0 & 2.3238 \end{bmatrix} \begin{bmatrix} x_1 \\ x_2 \\ x_3 \end{bmatrix} = \begin{bmatrix} 201.2677 \\ -15.7662 \\ 120.6533 \end{bmatrix}$$

with solutions

$$x_1 = \frac{201.2677}{6} = 33.5446, \qquad x_2 = \frac{-15.7662}{3.8333} = 4.1130,$$

$$x_3 = \frac{120.6533}{3.4348} = 35.1267.$$

6.3 Gauss Reduction Method in Terms of Matrix Transformations

The reduction effected by the algebraic manipulations described in the preceding two sections can be effected by matrix multiplication.

Let the original system of equations to be solved be (in matrix notation)

$$\mathscr{A}\mathscr{X} = \mathscr{B}, \tag{6.3.1}$$

where

$\mathscr{A} = (a_{ij})$; that is, $\mathscr{A}$ is a square matrix with the entry a_{ij} in the ith row and jth column

and

$$\left.\begin{array}{l} \mathscr{X} = (x_i) \\ \mathscr{B} = (b_i) \end{array}\right\} \text{ that is, } \mathscr{X} \text{ and } \mathscr{B} \text{ are column matrices or vectors.}$$

Then the first step in the Gauss reduction is to replace the elements below the diagonal in the first column of $\mathscr{A}$ by zeros. This can be accomplished by multiplying both sides of Equation 6.3.1 by the matrix $\mathscr{F}_1 = (t_{ij}^{(1)})$, where for i and $j = 1, \ldots, n$

$$t_{ii}^{(1)} = 1,$$

$$t_{i1}^{(1)} = -\frac{a_{i1}}{a_{11}} \quad \text{for} \quad i > 1, \tag{6.3.2}$$

$$t_{ij}^{(1)} = 0 \quad \text{otherwise.}$$

Equation 6.3.1 then becomes

$$\mathscr{F}_1\mathscr{A}\mathscr{X} = \mathscr{F}_1\mathscr{B} \tag{6.3.3}$$

with the first column reduced to zeros except for the diagonal term. Let $\mathscr{A}_1 = \mathscr{F}_1\mathscr{A} = (a_{ij}^{(1)})$, a matrix with the below-diagonal terms in the first column reduced to zero.

The second column is reduced to zeros below the diagonal by multiplying both sides of Equation 6.3.3 by $\mathscr{F}_2 = (t_{ij}^{(2)})$ where

$$t_{ii}^{(2)} = 1, \qquad t_{i2}^{(2)} = -\frac{a'_{i2}}{a'_{22}}, \quad i > 2, \tag{6.3.4}$$

$$t_{ij}^{(2)} = 0 \quad \text{otherwise.}$$

This gives

$$\mathscr{F}_2\mathscr{F}_1\mathscr{A}\mathscr{X} = \mathscr{F}_2\mathscr{F}_1\mathscr{B}. \tag{6.3.5}$$

Let $\mathscr{A}_2 = \mathscr{F}_2\mathscr{F}_1\mathscr{A} = (a_{ij}^{(2)})$. Then $\mathscr{A}_2$ is a matrix with the subdiagonal elements of the first two columns reduced to zero. In general, to reduce the kth column to zeros below the diagonal, it is necessary to form

$$\mathscr{A}_k = \mathscr{F}_k\mathscr{F}_{k-1} \cdots \mathscr{F}_2\mathscr{F}_1\mathscr{A}, \tag{6.3.6}$$

where

$$\mathscr{F} = (t_{ij}^{(k)})$$

and

$$t_{ii}^{(k)} = 1,$$

$$t_{ik}^{(k)} = -\frac{a_{ik}^{(k-1)}}{a_{kk}^{(k-1)}}, \qquad i > k, \tag{6.3.7}$$

$$t_{ij}^{(k)} = 0 \quad \text{otherwise.}$$

Hence, the first part of the Gauss method amounts to replacing Equation 6.3.1 by

$$\mathscr{A}_{n-1} = \mathscr{F}_{n-1}\mathscr{F}_{n-2} \cdots \mathscr{F}_2\mathscr{F}_1\mathscr{A}\mathscr{X} = \mathscr{F}_{n-1} \cdots \mathscr{F}_1\mathscr{B}.$$

EXAMPLE 6.3.1 Reduce the following system to one with zeros in all subdiagonal positions.

$$\begin{bmatrix} 3 & -1 & -2 \\ 2 & 4 & -1 \\ -1 & -2 & 5 \end{bmatrix} \begin{bmatrix} x_1 \\ x_2 \\ x_3 \end{bmatrix} \begin{bmatrix} 20 \\ 50 \\ -30 \end{bmatrix}$$

Solution: The first transformation matrix is

$$\mathscr{F}_1 = \begin{bmatrix} 1 & 0 & 0 \\ -\frac{2}{3} & 1 & 0 \\ +\frac{1}{3} & 0 & 1 \end{bmatrix}.$$

Then

$$\mathscr{A}_1 \mathscr{X} = \mathscr{F}_1 \mathscr{A} \mathscr{X} = \begin{bmatrix} 1 & 0 & 0 \\ -\frac{2}{3} & 1 & 0 \\ \frac{1}{3} & 0 & 1 \end{bmatrix} \begin{bmatrix} 3 & -1 & -2 \\ 2 & 4 & -1 \\ -1 & -2 & 5 \end{bmatrix} \begin{bmatrix} x_1 \\ x_2 \\ x_3 \end{bmatrix}$$

$$= \begin{bmatrix} 1 & 0 & 0 \\ -\frac{2}{3} & 1 & 0 \\ \frac{1}{3} & 0 & 1 \end{bmatrix} \begin{bmatrix} 20 \\ 50 \\ -30 \end{bmatrix}$$

or

$$\mathscr{A}_1 \mathscr{X} = \begin{bmatrix} 3 & -1 & -2 \\ 0 & \frac{14}{3} & \frac{1}{3} \\ 0 & -\frac{7}{3} & \frac{13}{3} \end{bmatrix} \begin{bmatrix} x_1 \\ x_2 \\ x_3 \end{bmatrix} = \begin{bmatrix} 20 \\ \frac{110}{3} \\ -\frac{70}{3} \end{bmatrix}.$$

The next transformation matrix is

$$\mathscr{F}_2 = \begin{bmatrix} 1 & 0 & 0 \\ 0 & 1 & 0 \\ 0 & \frac{1}{2} & 1 \end{bmatrix},$$

and

$$\mathscr{A}_2 \mathscr{X} = \mathscr{F}_2 \mathscr{F}_1 \mathscr{A} \mathscr{X}$$

$$= \begin{bmatrix} 1 & 0 & 0 \\ 0 & 1 & 0 \\ 0 & \frac{1}{2} & 1 \end{bmatrix} \begin{bmatrix} 3 & -1 & -2 \\ 0 & \frac{14}{3} & \frac{1}{3} \\ 0 & -\frac{7}{3} & \frac{13}{3} \end{bmatrix} \begin{bmatrix} x_1 \\ x_2 \\ x_3 \end{bmatrix} = \begin{bmatrix} 1 & 0 & 0 \\ 0 & 1 & 0 \\ 0 & \frac{1}{2} & 1 \end{bmatrix} \begin{bmatrix} 20 \\ \frac{110}{3} \\ -\frac{70}{3} \end{bmatrix}$$

or

$$\mathscr{A}_2\mathscr{X} = \begin{bmatrix} 3 & -1 & -2 \\ 0 & \frac{14}{3} & \frac{1}{3} \\ 0 & 0 & \frac{9}{2} \end{bmatrix} \begin{bmatrix} x_1 \\ x_2 \\ x_3 \end{bmatrix} = \begin{bmatrix} 20 \\ \frac{110}{3} \\ -5 \end{bmatrix}.$$

If the final matrix of the Gauss-Jordan Method, Equation 6.2.4, is sought, the transformation is of the form

$$\mathscr{S}_{n-1}\mathscr{F}_{n-1}\mathscr{S}_{n-2}\mathscr{F}_{n-2}\cdots\mathscr{S}_2\mathscr{F}_2\mathscr{S}_1\mathscr{F}_1\mathscr{A}, \qquad (6.3.8)$$

where the $\mathscr{S}_k$ matrices are $n \times n$ identity matrices with the upper off-diagonal terms in the $(k + 1)$ column, $a_{j,k+1}$, with $j < k + 1$, replaced by

$$s_{j,k+1}^{(k)} = -\frac{a_{j,k+1}}{a_{k+1,k+1}}, \qquad (6.3.9)$$

where $a_{j,k+1}$ and $a_{k+1,k+1}$ are the elements in the jth and $(k + 1)$st rows, respectively, in the $(k + 1)$st column of the matrix

$$\mathscr{F}_k\mathscr{S}_{k-1}\mathscr{F}_{k-1}\cdots\mathscr{S}_2\mathscr{F}_2\mathscr{S}_1\mathscr{F}_1\mathscr{A}. \qquad (6.3.10)$$

For example, in this last equation

$$\mathscr{S}_1 = \begin{bmatrix} 1 & -\dfrac{a_{12}}{a'_{22}} & 0 & \cdots \\ 0 & 1 & 0 & \cdots \\ \vdots & & & \vdots \\ 0 & 0 & & \cdots & 1 \end{bmatrix} \qquad (6.3.11)$$

and

$$\mathscr{S}_2 = \begin{bmatrix} 1 & 0 & -\dfrac{a_{13}}{a'_{33}} & \cdots \\ 0 & 1 & -\dfrac{a'_{23}}{a'_{33}} & \cdots \\ 0 & 0 & 1 & \cdots \\ 0 & 0 & 0 & \cdots & 1 \end{bmatrix}. \qquad (6.3.12)$$

Note that at each step the $\mathscr{S}_k$ matrix is formed using the elements in the matrix resulting from the multiplication by $\mathscr{F}_k$.

EXAMPLE 6.3.2 Reduce the system of Example 6.3.1 to diagonal form by matrix transformations.

Solution: Making use of the results of the first step as carried out in Example 6.3.1.

$$\mathscr{A}_1 \mathscr{X} = \begin{bmatrix} 3 & -1 & -2 \\ 0 & \frac{14}{3} & \frac{1}{3} \\ 0 & -\frac{7}{3} & \frac{31}{3} \end{bmatrix} \begin{bmatrix} x_1 \\ x_2 \\ x_3 \end{bmatrix} = \mathscr{F}_1 \mathscr{B} = \begin{bmatrix} 20 \\ \frac{110}{3} \\ -\frac{70}{3} \end{bmatrix}.$$

Then

$$\mathscr{S}_1 = \begin{bmatrix} 1 & \frac{3}{14} & 0 \\ 0 & 1 & 0 \\ 0 & 0 & 1 \end{bmatrix},$$

and

$$\mathscr{S}_1 \mathscr{F}_1 \mathscr{A} \mathscr{X} = \begin{bmatrix} 1 & \frac{3}{14} & 0 \\ 0 & 1 & 0 \\ 0 & 0 & 1 \end{bmatrix} \begin{bmatrix} 3 & -1 & -2 \\ 0 & \frac{14}{3} & \frac{1}{3} \\ 0 & -\frac{7}{3} & \frac{13}{3} \end{bmatrix} \begin{bmatrix} x_1 \\ x_2 \\ x_3 \end{bmatrix} = \begin{bmatrix} 1 & \frac{3}{14} & 0 \\ 0 & 1 & 0 \\ 0 & 0 & 1 \end{bmatrix} \begin{bmatrix} 20 \\ \frac{110}{3} \\ -\frac{70}{3} \end{bmatrix}$$

or

$$\mathscr{S}_1 \mathscr{F}_1 \mathscr{A} \mathscr{X} = \begin{bmatrix} 3 & 0 & -\frac{27}{14} \\ 0 & \frac{14}{3} & \frac{1}{3} \\ 0 & -\frac{7}{3} & \frac{13}{3} \end{bmatrix} \begin{bmatrix} x_1 \\ x_2 \\ x_3 \end{bmatrix} = \begin{bmatrix} \frac{195}{7} \\ \frac{110}{3} \\ -\frac{70}{3} \end{bmatrix}.$$

Now

$$\mathscr{F}_2 = \begin{bmatrix} 1 & 0 & 0 \\ 0 & 1 & 0 \\ 0 & \frac{1}{2} & 1 \end{bmatrix},$$

and

$$\mathscr{F}_2 \mathscr{S}_1 \mathscr{F}_1 \mathscr{A} \mathscr{X} = \begin{bmatrix} 1 & 0 & 0 \\ 0 & 1 & 0 \\ 0 & \frac{1}{2} & 1 \end{bmatrix} \begin{bmatrix} 3 & 0 & -\frac{27}{14} \\ 0 & \frac{14}{3} & \frac{1}{3} \\ 0 & -\frac{7}{3} & \frac{13}{3} \end{bmatrix} \begin{bmatrix} x_1 \\ x_2 \\ x_3 \end{bmatrix}$$

$$= \begin{bmatrix} 1 & 0 & 0 \\ 0 & 1 & 0 \\ 0 & \frac{1}{2} & 1 \end{bmatrix} \begin{bmatrix} \frac{195}{7} \\ \frac{110}{3} \\ -\frac{70}{3} \end{bmatrix}$$

or

$$\mathscr{F}_2 \mathscr{S}_1 \mathscr{F}_1 \mathscr{X} = \begin{bmatrix} 3 & 0 & -\frac{27}{14} \\ 0 & \frac{14}{3} & \frac{1}{3} \\ 0 & 0 & \frac{27}{6} \end{bmatrix} \begin{bmatrix} x_1 \\ x_2 \\ x_3 \end{bmatrix} = \begin{bmatrix} \frac{195}{7} \\ \frac{110}{3} \\ -\frac{15}{3} \end{bmatrix}.$$

From this matrix

$$\mathscr{S}_2 = \begin{bmatrix} 1 & 0 & +\frac{3}{7} \\ 0 & 1 & -\frac{2}{27} \\ 0 & 0 & 1 \end{bmatrix},$$

and

$$\mathscr{S}_2 \mathscr{F}_2 \mathscr{S}_1 \mathscr{F}_1 \mathscr{A} \mathscr{X} = \begin{bmatrix} 1 & 0 & \frac{3}{7} \\ 0 & 1 & -\frac{2}{27} \\ 0 & 0 & 1 \end{bmatrix} \begin{bmatrix} 3 & 0 & -\frac{27}{14} \\ 0 & \frac{14}{3} & \frac{1}{3} \\ 0 & 0 & \frac{9}{2} \end{bmatrix} \begin{bmatrix} x_1 \\ x_2 \\ x_3 \end{bmatrix}$$

$$= \begin{bmatrix} 1 & 0 & \frac{3}{7} \\ 0 & 1 & -\frac{2}{27} \\ 0 & 0 & 1 \end{bmatrix} \begin{bmatrix} \frac{195}{7} \\ \frac{110}{3} \\ -\frac{15}{3} \end{bmatrix}$$

or

$$\mathscr{S}_2 \mathscr{F}_2 \mathscr{S}_1 \mathscr{F}_1 \mathscr{A} \mathscr{X} = \begin{bmatrix} 3 & 0 & 0 \\ 0 & \frac{14}{3} & 0 \\ 0 & 0 & \frac{9}{2} \end{bmatrix} \begin{bmatrix} x_1 \\ x_2 \\ x_3 \end{bmatrix} = \begin{bmatrix} \frac{180}{7} \\ \frac{1000}{27} \\ -5 \end{bmatrix}.$$

Obviously the matrix-transformation technique constitutes another method for organizing the computation in an orderly fashion and perhaps is of more value theoretically than for actual computations.

Exercises

1. Given the equation

$$\mathscr{A} \mathscr{X} = \mathscr{B},$$

where $\mathscr{A} = (a_{ij})$ is an $n \times n$ matrix, $\mathscr{X}$ and $\mathscr{B}$ are $n \times 1$ matrices, to reduce the entries below the diagonal to zero in the kth column it is necessary to multiply the kth row by $\dfrac{a'_{ik}}{a'_{kk}}$. Since a'_{ik} and a'_{kk} are obtained by arithmetical manipulations in eliminating the previous subdiagonal elements, each will be in error by an amount ϵ_{ik} and ϵ_{kk} say. What effect does the size of a'_{kk} have on the error in $\dfrac{a'_{ik}}{a'_{kk}}$?

2. It is known that

$$a_{im} \leftarrow a_{im} - a_{km} \frac{a_{ik}}{a_{kk}};$$

that is, a_{im} is replaced by the quantity on the right side of the arrow. If a_{im} is in error by ϵ_{im}, and a_{km} is in error by ϵ_{km}, etc., what is the error in the new value of a_{im}?

6.4 Matrix Inversion by the Gauss Reduction Technique

If, in place of a set of linear equations to be solved, the problem is to invert a matrix, $\mathscr{A}$, the Gauss reduction technique can be used very effectively.

In terms of matrix transformations the problem is to find a transformation matrix, $\mathscr{F}$, such that

$$\mathscr{F}\mathscr{A} = \mathscr{I} \tag{6.4.1}$$

so that

$$\mathscr{F}\mathscr{I} = \mathscr{F} = \mathscr{A}^{-1}, \tag{6.4.2}$$

where $\mathscr{I}$ is the $n \times n$ identity matrix.

If the transformations of Equation 6.3.8 are used on the augmented matrix

$$\mathscr{A}_a = \begin{bmatrix} a_{11} & a_{12} & \cdots & a_{1n} & 1 & 0 & \cdots & 0 \\ a_{21} & a_{22} & \cdots & a_{2n} & 0 & 1 & \cdots & 0 \\ \vdots & & & & & & & \vdots \\ a_{n1} & a_{n2} & \cdots & a_{nn} & 0 & 0 & \cdots & 1 \end{bmatrix}, \tag{6.4.3}$$

a new augmented matrix ($n \times 2n$) of the form

$$\mathscr{A}_{a1} = \begin{bmatrix} a_{11} & 0 & \cdots & 0 & c_{11} & c_{12} & \cdots & c_{1n} \\ 0 & a'_{22} & \cdots & 0 & c_{21} & c_{22} & \cdots & c_{2n} \\ \vdots & & & & & & & \vdots \\ 0 & 0 & \cdots & a'_{nn} & c_{n1} & c_{n2} & \cdots & c_{nn} \end{bmatrix} \tag{6.4.4}$$

results.

If now each row of the augmented matrix is divided by the diagonal term in that row, in the left-hand half matrix, the result is

$$\mathscr{A}_{a2} = \begin{bmatrix} 1 & 0 & \cdots & 0 & c'_{11} & c'_{12} & \cdots & c'_{1n} \\ 0 & 1 & \cdots & 0 & c'_{21} & c'_{22} & \cdots & c'_{2n} \\ \vdots & & & & & & & \vdots \\ 0 & 0 & \cdots & 1 & c'_{n1} & c'_{n2} & \cdots & c'_{n2} \end{bmatrix} \tag{6.4.5}$$

or

$$\mathscr{A}_{a2} = [\mathscr{I}\mathscr{C}] = [\mathscr{F}\mathscr{A}\mathscr{F}\mathscr{I}], \tag{6.4.6}$$

where

$$\mathscr{F} = \mathscr{F}_n \mathscr{S}_{n-1} \mathscr{F}_{n-1} \cdots \mathscr{S}_1 \mathscr{F}_1 \tag{6.4.7}$$

and

$$\mathscr{F}_n = \begin{bmatrix} \dfrac{1}{a_{11}} & 0 & \cdots & 0 \\ 0 & \dfrac{1}{a_{22}} & \cdots & 0 \\ \vdots & & & \vdots \\ 0 & 0 & \cdots & \dfrac{1}{a_{nn}} \end{bmatrix}. \tag{6.4.8}$$

Since

$$\mathscr{F}\mathscr{A} = \mathscr{I}, \tag{6.4.9}$$

then

$$\mathscr{F} = \mathscr{A}^{-1}. \tag{6.4.10}$$

But

$$\mathscr{F}\mathscr{I} = \mathscr{C} = \mathscr{F}; \tag{6.4.11}$$

hence

$$\mathscr{C} = \mathscr{A}^{-1}. \tag{6.4.12}$$

EXAMPLE 6.4.1   Use the matrix-transformation form of the Gauss–Jordan reduction method to find the inverse of the coefficient matrix of Example 6.3.1

Solution: The given matrix is

$$\begin{bmatrix} 3 & -1 & -2 \\ 2 & 4 & -1 \\ -1 & -2 & 5 \end{bmatrix}.$$

Hence the augmented matrix is

$$\mathscr{A}_a = \begin{bmatrix} 3 & -1 & -2 & 1 & 0 & 0 \\ 2 & 4 & -1 & 0 & 1 & 0 \\ -1 & -2 & 5 & 0 & 0 & 1 \end{bmatrix}.$$

The $\mathscr{S}$ and $\mathscr{F}$ matrices are just those in Examples 6.3.1 and 6.3.2. Then

$$\mathscr{F}_1\mathscr{A}_a = \begin{bmatrix} 1 & 0 & 0 \\ -\frac{2}{3} & 1 & 0 \\ \frac{1}{3} & 0 & 1 \end{bmatrix} \begin{bmatrix} 3 & -1 & -2 & 1 & 0 & 0 \\ 2 & 4 & -1 & 0 & 1 & 0 \\ -1 & -2 & 5 & 0 & 0 & 1 \end{bmatrix}$$

$$= \begin{bmatrix} 3 & -1 & -2 & 1 & 0 & 0 \\ 0 & \frac{14}{3} & \frac{1}{3} & -\frac{2}{3} & 1 & 0 \\ 0 & -\frac{7}{3} & \frac{13}{3} & \frac{1}{3} & 0 & 1 \end{bmatrix},$$

$$\mathscr{S}_1\mathscr{F}_1\mathscr{A}_a = \begin{bmatrix} 1 & \frac{3}{14} & 0 \\ 0 & 1 & 0 \\ 0 & 0 & 1 \end{bmatrix} \begin{bmatrix} 3 & -1 & -2 & 1 & 0 & 0 \\ 0 & \frac{14}{3} & \frac{1}{3} & -\frac{2}{3} & 1 & 0 \\ 0 & -\frac{7}{3} & \frac{13}{3} & \frac{1}{3} & 0 & 1 \end{bmatrix}$$

$$= \begin{bmatrix} 3 & 0 & -\frac{27}{14} & \frac{6}{7} & \frac{3}{14} & 0 \\ 0 & \frac{14}{3} & \frac{1}{3} & -\frac{2}{3} & 1 & 0 \\ 0 & -\frac{7}{3} & \frac{13}{3} & \frac{1}{3} & 0 & 1 \end{bmatrix},$$

$$\mathscr{F}_2\mathscr{S}_1\mathscr{F}_1\mathscr{A}_a = \begin{bmatrix} 1 & 0 & 0 \\ 0 & 1 & 0 \\ 0 & \frac{1}{2} & 1 \end{bmatrix} \begin{bmatrix} 3 & 0 & -\frac{27}{14} & \frac{6}{7} & \frac{3}{14} & 0 \\ 0 & \frac{14}{3} & \frac{1}{3} & -\frac{2}{3} & 1 & 0 \\ 0 & -\frac{7}{3} & \frac{13}{3} & \frac{1}{3} & 0 & 1 \end{bmatrix},$$

$$= \begin{bmatrix} 3 & 0 & -\frac{27}{14} & \frac{6}{7} & \frac{3}{14} & 0 \\ 0 & \frac{14}{3} & \frac{1}{3} & -\frac{2}{3} & 1 & 0 \\ 0 & 0 & \frac{9}{2} & 0 & \frac{1}{2} & 1 \end{bmatrix},$$

and finally

$$\mathscr{S}_2\mathscr{F}_2\mathscr{S}_1\mathscr{F}_1\mathscr{A}_a = \begin{bmatrix} 1 & 0 & \frac{3}{7} \\ 0 & 1 & -\frac{2}{27} \\ 0 & 0 & 1 \end{bmatrix} \begin{bmatrix} 3 & 0 & -\frac{27}{14} & \frac{6}{7} & \frac{3}{14} & 0 \\ 0 & \frac{14}{3} & \frac{1}{3} & -\frac{2}{3} & 1 & 0 \\ 0 & 0 & \frac{9}{2} & 0 & \frac{1}{2} & 1 \end{bmatrix}$$

$$= \begin{bmatrix} 3 & 0 & 0 & \frac{6}{7} & \frac{3}{7} & \frac{3}{7} \\ 0 & \frac{14}{3} & 0 & -\frac{2}{3} & \frac{26}{27} & -\frac{2}{27} \\ 0 & 0 & \frac{9}{2} & 0 & \frac{1}{2} & 1 \end{bmatrix}.$$

Dividing each row by the left-hand diagonal element in the row, or multiplying this last result by $\mathscr{F}_n$, as defined in Equation 6.4.8, to obtain

$\mathscr{F}\mathscr{A}_a$, where $\mathscr{F}$ is as defined in Equation 6.4.7, gives the result

$$\mathscr{F}\mathscr{A}_a = \begin{bmatrix} \frac{1}{3} & 0 & 0 \\ 0 & \frac{3}{14} & 0 \\ 0 & 0 & \frac{2}{9} \end{bmatrix} \begin{bmatrix} 3 & 0 & 0 & \frac{6}{7} & \frac{3}{7} & \frac{3}{7} \\ 0 & \frac{14}{3} & 0 & -\frac{2}{3} & \frac{26}{27} & -\frac{2}{27} \\ 0 & 0 & \frac{9}{2} & 0 & \frac{1}{2} & 1 \end{bmatrix}$$

$$= \begin{bmatrix} 1 & 0 & 0 & \frac{2}{7} & \frac{1}{7} & \frac{1}{7} \\ 0 & 1 & 0 & -\frac{1}{7} & \frac{13}{63} & -\frac{1}{63} \\ 0 & 0 & 1 & 0 & \frac{1}{9} & \frac{2}{9} \end{bmatrix},$$

from which, by Equations 6.4.9 through 6.4.12,

$$\mathscr{A}^{-1} = \begin{bmatrix} \frac{2}{7} & \frac{1}{7} & \frac{1}{7} \\ -\frac{1}{7} & \frac{13}{63} & -\frac{1}{63} \\ 0 & \frac{1}{9} & \frac{2}{9} \end{bmatrix}.$$

Exercise

If $\mathscr{F}\mathscr{A} = \mathscr{I}$ for an $n \times n$ matrix $\mathscr{A}$ and $\mathscr{F}$ a product of transformation matrices of the kind defined in Equations 6.3.2, 6.3.4, 6.3.11, and 6.3.12, show that $\mathscr{A}\mathscr{F} = \mathscr{I}$.

6.5 Gauss Reduction on a Digital Computer

A digital computer program to use the Gauss reduction method to solve a set of equations or to form a matrix inverse is not basically difficult in the sense of requiring complex or unusual algorithms. The operations in such a program are all straightforward divisions, multiplications and additions and it is only the necessity for many loops with variable counters which complicates the writing of the program.

The order of operations as given in Section 6.1 seems to be the simplest to program as well as to minimize the number of operations involved and thus minimize time and maximize accuracy.

The entire process of eliminating the subdiagonal terms of the matrix in Equation 6.1.2 can be summarized in a way which lends itself to programming on a computer. First, for convenience, let $b_i = a_{i,n+1}$ for $i = 1, \ldots, n$. Then the following computation must be performed:

Execute statement A for $j = 1, \ldots, n - 1$.

Execute statement A for $k = j + 1, \ldots, n$.

Execute statement A for $i = j, \ldots, n + 1$.

Statement A: $a_{ki} \leftarrow a_{ki} - a_{ji} \dfrac{a_{kj}}{a_{jj}}$.

This cryptic set of statements is similar to statements used in FORTRAN and ALGOL and needs some explanation. Statement A means to replace the value of a_{ki} by that which is calculated on the right side of the arrow. The three "Execute" statements simply require that Statement A be executed for all the combinations of j, k, and i possible with the ranges specified for each subscript, with i varying most rapidly, k less rapidly, and j the least rapidly. At the termination of this procedure, all terms below the diagonal of the matrix in Equation 6.1.2 will have been reduced to zeroes.

Implicit in this process are certain checks. Thus, since a division by a_{jj} occurs in each execution of statement A, it must be the case that $a_{jj} \neq 0$. If this is not so, then each element in the jth column below the jth row should be examined. As soon as a nonzero element is encountered, the jth row and the row with a nonzero entry in column j should be interchanged, and the process executed. If there is no nonzero element below the jth row in the jth column when $a_{jj} = 0$, the matrix is singular and the process should terminate.

The authors' experience with this and other methods for obtaining a matrix inverse on a digital computer suggests that, although this method leaves much to be desired, particularly insofar as accuracy is concerned, it is still the most satisfactory method thus far available. A monumental error analysis of this method of inversion was carried out by von Neumann and Goldstine.[*] As the matrix $\mathscr{A}$ becomes more nearly singular, that is, as the determinant of $\mathscr{A}$ becomes more nearly zero, the inversion process discussed above gives poorer results.

6.6 Gauss-Seidel Iteration and Relaxation

The direct methods of solution of a set of linear equations discussed so far in this chapter are methods which should lead to a correct answer at the end of a particular number of steps, this number being a function of the method used. Because of the large number of steps involved, round-off errors are, in some problems, so great that the resulting answers are not sufficiently accurate. In such cases, some type of iteration method may be used to obtain more accurate results.

One such iteration method is that in which the ith equation in a set of linear equations

$$
\begin{aligned}
a_{11}x_1 + a_{12}x_2 + \cdots + a_{1n}x_n &= b_1, \\
a_{21}x_1 + a_{22}x_2 + \cdots + a_{2n}x_n &= b_2, \\
&\ \vdots \\
a_{n1}x_1 + a_{n2}x_2 + \cdots + a_{nn}x_n &= b_n
\end{aligned}
\tag{6.6.1}
$$

[*] John von Neumann and H. H. Goldstine, "Numerical Inverting of Matrices of High Order," *Bull. Am. Math. Soc.*, vol. **53**, pp. 1021–1099 (1947).

is solved for x_i. Thus, the equations in Equation 6.6.1 are rewritten as

$$x_1 = \frac{1}{a_{11}}[b_1 - a_{12}x_2 - \cdots - a_{1n}x_n],$$

$$x_2 = \frac{1}{a_{22}}[b_2 - a_{21}x_1 - a_{23}x_3 - \cdots - a_{2n}x_n], \qquad (6.6.2)$$

$$\vdots$$

$$x_n = \frac{1}{a_{nn}}[b_n - a_{n1}x_1 - a_{n2}x_2 - \cdots - a_{n,n-1}x_{n-1}].$$

An estimated value for each x_i is substituted into Equation 6.6.2 and new values of the x_i calculated thereby. This process is repeated, replacing the x_i estimates by the newly calculated values. The process may be terminated when the new values calculated do not differ from the previously calculated values by more than some arbitrarily specified values.

The original estimated values may be arbitrary or they may be calculated in some manner. One method of calculating these estimates which is particularly applicable if the diagonal terms, a_{kk}, in the coefficient matrix are large relative to the nondiagonal terms, $a_{kj}, j \neq k$, is to calculate x_k as

$$x_k = \frac{b_k}{a_{kk}}. \qquad (6.6.3)$$

EXAMPLE 6.6.1   Use the iteration method described in the preceding discussion to find the first four estimates to the solution of the set of equations

$$4x_1 + x_2 + 2x_3 = 2,$$

$$2x_1 + 6x_2 + x_3 = 3,$$

$$x_1 + x_2 + 4x_3 = 1.$$

Carry calculations to six decimals.

Solution: A first estimate, by Equation 6.6.3, is

$$x_{11} = \tfrac{2}{4} = 0.5,$$

$$x_{21} = \tfrac{3}{6} = 0.5,$$

$$x_{31} = \tfrac{1}{4} = 0.25.$$

For this problem, Equation 6.6.2 can be written

$$x_1 = \tfrac{1}{4}[2 - x_2 - 2x_3],$$

$$x_2 = \tfrac{1}{6}[3 - 2x_1 - x_3],$$

$$x_3 = \tfrac{1}{4}[1 - x_1 - x_2].$$

Using the first estimates in this set of equations gives

$$x_{12} = \tfrac{1}{4}[2 - 1(0.5) - 2(0.25)] = 0.25,$$
$$x_{22} = \tfrac{1}{6}[3 - 2(0.5) - 1(0.25)] = 0.291667,$$
$$x_{32} = \tfrac{1}{4}[1 - 1(0.5) - 1(0.5)] = 0.$$

A third estimate is found, by using the last values of the variables in Equation 6.6.2, as

$$x_{13} = \tfrac{1}{4}[2 - 0.291667 - 0] = 0.427083,$$
$$x_{23} = \tfrac{1}{6}[3 - 0.5 - 0] = 0.416667,$$
$$x_{33} = \tfrac{1}{4}[1 - 0.25 - 0.291667] = 0.114584.$$

Finally, a fourth estimate is

$$x_{14} = \tfrac{1}{4}[2 - 0.416667 - 0.229168] = 0.338541,$$
$$x_{24} = \tfrac{1}{6}[3 - 0.854166 - 0.114583] = 0.338542,$$
$$x_{34} = \tfrac{1}{4}[1 - 0.427083 - 0.416667] = 0.039063.$$

The solution to this set of equations, by the direct method of determinants, is found to be, to six decimal place accuracy,

$$x_1 = 0.376623,$$
$$x_2 = 0.363636,$$
$$x_3 = 0.064935.$$

An examination of the estimates indicates that the process seems to be a converging one is this case.

In a variation of the general method of the preceding discussion, the most recently calculated value of a particular x_k is used in all subsequent calculations in contrast to the use of a given set of estimated values in the total set of equations. This method is often called the Gauss-Seidel method or simply the Seidel method. This method, when it is convergent, converges more rapidly, as is seen in the following example.

EXAMPLE 6.6.2   Repeat the problem of Example 6.6.1, using the Seidel method.

Solution: Using the first estimates as found in Example 6.6.1, a first time through the set of equations in Equation 6.6.2 yields the values

$$x_{12} = \tfrac{1}{4}[2 - 1(0.5) - 2(0.25)] = 0.25,$$
$$x_{22} = \tfrac{1}{6}[3 - 2(0.25) - 1(0.25)] = 0.375,$$
$$x_{32} = \tfrac{1}{4}[1 - 1(0.25) - 1(0.375)] = 0.09375.$$

A second and third application of the process yields

$$x_{13} = \tfrac{1}{4}[2 - 0.375 - 0.1875] = 0.359375,$$

$$x_{23} = \tfrac{1}{6}[3 - 0.71875 - 0.09375] = 0.364583,$$

$$x_{33} = \tfrac{1}{4}[1 - 0.359375 - 0.364583] = 0.069011,$$

$$x_{14} = \tfrac{1}{4}[2 - 0.364583 - 0.138022] = 0.374349,$$

$$x_{24} = \tfrac{1}{6}[3 - 0.748698 - 0.069011] = 0.363715,$$

$$x_{34} = \tfrac{1}{4}[1 - 0.374349 - 0.363715] = 0.065484.$$

Comparison of these results with the results in Example 6.6.1 indicates that the rate of convergence of the Seidel method for this problem is indeed more rapid than for the previous method.

A relaxation method is an iteration method in which residuals, R_i, are defined for the set of equations given in Equation 6.6.1 as

$$R_1 = b_1 - a_{11}x_1 - a_{12}x_2 \cdots -a_{1n}x_n,$$

$$R_2 = b_2 - a_{12}x_1 - a_{22}x_2 \cdots -a_{2n}x_n, \qquad (6.6.4)$$

$$\vdots$$

$$R_n = b_n - a_{n1}x_1 - a_{n2}x_2 \cdots -a_{nn}x_n.$$

The unknowns $x_1, x_2, \ldots, x_n$ are first estimated, the residuals calculated, then the estimated values of the unknowns are successively modified in such a way as to reduce the residuals to zero.

The Gauss-Seidel method is actually a relaxation method since an equation in the set of Equation 6.6.2 can be rewritten in terms of the new estimate, x_k^*, as

$$x_k^* = \frac{1}{a_{kk}}(b_k - a_{kk}x_1 - a_{k2}x_2 - \cdots - a_{kn}x_n)$$

$$= \frac{1}{a_{kk}}(R_k + a_{kk}x_k) = x_k + \frac{R_k}{a_{kk}}. \qquad (6.6.5)$$

In order to take full advantage of the possibilities of a relaxation method, the residuals at each step should be examined. The largest residual may then be reduced to zero, or some alternative procedure used if such appears to be desirable.

This method, requiring as it does a decision at each step, is more difficult to adapt to automatic-computer use. However, the Gauss-Seidel method can be programmed for an automatic computer with little difficulty. The real problem in this method is that of convergence.

Exercise

Let $\mathscr{A}\mathscr{X} = \mathscr{B}$ be the matrix form of a system of n linear equations in n unknowns. Let $\mathscr{X}_i$ be the approximate solution obtained by the ith iteration of some interative technique. Let $\mathscr{A}\mathscr{X}_i = \mathscr{B}_i$ and let

$$\mathscr{X}_{i+1} - \mathscr{X}_i = \begin{bmatrix} x_{1,i+1} - x_{1,i} \\ x_{2,i+1} - x_{2,i} \\ . \\ . \\ . \\ x_{n,i+1} - x_{n,i} \end{bmatrix},$$

where x_{ji} is the jth component of $\mathscr{X}_i$. If in absolute value the maximum component of $\mathscr{X}_{i+1} - \mathscr{X}_i$ is smaller than ϵ, denoted by $|\mathscr{X}_{i+1} - \mathscr{X}_i| < \epsilon$, what then is a bound for $|\mathscr{B}_{i+1} - \mathscr{B}_i|$?

The tests for convergence of the Gauss-Seidel method are all fairly intricate. However, two tests which do not require extensive mathematical background are given here.

First, if the system of equations in Equation 6.6.1 has the property

$$|a_{ii}| > \sum_{\substack{j=1 \\ j \neq i}}^{n} |a_{ij}|, \qquad i = 1, 2, \ldots, n, \tag{6.6.6}$$

then the Gauss-Seidel method produces a convergent sequence of approximations to the solution of Equation 6.6.1. The proof is somewhat beyond the scope of this book. However, the essential steps are given here. First, Equation 6.6.1 can be rewritten in matrix form as

$$\mathscr{A}\mathscr{X} = \mathscr{B}, \tag{6.6.7}$$

where $\mathscr{A}$ is the $n \times n$ matrix,

$$\mathscr{A} = \begin{bmatrix} a_{11} & a_{12} & \cdots & a_{1n} \\ a_{21} & a_{22} & \cdots & a_{2n} \\ a_{n1} & a_{n2} & \cdots & a_{nn} \end{bmatrix} = [a_{ij}]; \tag{6.6.8}$$

$\mathscr{B}$ is the column matrix or vector,

$$\mathscr{B} = \begin{bmatrix} b_1 \\ b_2 \\ . \\ . \\ . \\ b_n \end{bmatrix}, \tag{6.6.9}$$

while $\mathscr{X}$ is the column matrix

$$\mathscr{X} = \begin{bmatrix} x_1 \\ x_2 \\ \cdot \\ \cdot \\ \cdot \\ x_n \end{bmatrix}. \tag{6.6.10}$$

Then the Gauss-Seidel method requires that $\mathscr{A}\mathscr{X} = \mathscr{B}$ be solved for $\mathscr{X}$ as

$$\mathscr{X} = \mathscr{B} - \mathscr{C}\mathscr{X}, \tag{6.6.11}$$

where $\mathscr{C}$ is the $n \times n$ matrix $\mathscr{C} = [c_{ij}]$ with $c_{ii} = 0$ and $c_{ij} = -\dfrac{a_{ij}}{a_{ii}}$ for
for $i, j = 1, 2, \ldots, n$. Then let $x_1^{(m)}, \ldots, x_n^{(m)}$ be the mth approximation
to the solution of $\mathscr{A}\mathscr{X} = \mathscr{B}$ obtained by the Gauss-Seidel method, and let

$$\mathscr{X}^{(m)} = \begin{bmatrix} x_1^{(m)} \\ x_2^{(m)} \\ \cdot \\ \cdot \\ \cdot \\ x_n^{(m)} \end{bmatrix}. \tag{6.6.12}$$

Then the Gauss-Seidel iteration is defined by

$$\mathscr{X}^{(m)} = \mathscr{B} - \mathscr{C}\mathscr{X}^{(m-1)}. \tag{6.6.13}$$

Repeatedly applying this equation, there follows

$$\begin{aligned}
\mathscr{X}^{(m)} = \mathscr{B} - \mathscr{C}\mathscr{X}^{(m-1)} &= \mathscr{B} - \mathscr{C}(\mathscr{B} - \mathscr{C}\mathscr{X}^{(m-2)}) \\
&= \mathscr{B} - \mathscr{C}\mathscr{B} + \mathscr{C}^2\mathscr{X}^{(m-2)} \\
& \qquad\qquad \cdot \\
& \qquad\qquad \cdot \\
& \qquad\qquad \cdot \\
&= \mathscr{B} - \mathscr{C}\mathscr{B} + \mathscr{C}^2\mathscr{B} - \mathscr{C}^3\mathscr{B} \cdots + \\
& \quad + (-1)^{m-2}\mathscr{C}^{m-2}\mathscr{B} + (-1)^{m-1}\mathscr{X}^{(1)}. \quad (6.6.14)
\end{aligned}$$

From this last equation it follows that

$$\begin{aligned}
\mathscr{X}^{(m+j)} - \mathscr{X}^{(m)} = ((-1)^{m+j-1}\mathscr{C}^{m+j-1} &- (-1)^{m-1}\mathscr{C}^{m-1})\mathscr{X}^{(1)} + (-1)^{m-1} \\
\times [\mathscr{C}^{m-1} - \mathscr{C}^m &+ \mathscr{C}^{m+1} + \cdots + (-1)^{j-1}\mathscr{C}^{m+j-1}]\mathscr{B}.
\end{aligned}$$
$$\tag{6.6.15}$$

It can be shown* that for $|a_{ii}| > \sum_{\substack{j=1 \\ j \neq i}}^{n} |a_{ij}|$ for $i = 1, 2, \ldots, n$ the matrix $\mathscr{C}^m \to 0$ as $m \to \infty$. Hence for m large enough and for all j, $\mathscr{X}^{(m+j)} - \mathscr{X}^{(m)}$ becomes arbitrarily close to the zero vector, i.e., an $n \times 1$ matrix all of whose entries are zeros. Hence the sequence $\mathscr{X}^{(1)}, \mathscr{X}^{(2)}, \mathscr{X}^{(3)}, \ldots$ converges. In fact the sequence converges to the solution of $\mathscr{A}\mathscr{X} = \mathscr{B}$. For since the sequence converges, then for m large enough $\mathscr{X}^{(m)}$ becomes arbitrarily close to $\mathscr{B} - \mathscr{C}\mathscr{X}^{(m)}$, and in the limit the equation $\mathscr{X} = \mathscr{B} - \mathscr{C}\mathscr{X}$ is satisfied. Hence, the limit of the sequence is indeed the solution of $\mathscr{X} = \mathscr{B} - \mathscr{C}\mathscr{X}$ or $\mathscr{A}\mathscr{X} = \mathscr{B}$.

EXAMPLE: Will the Gauss-Seidel method converge for the system

$$4x + 1y + 2z = 3,$$
$$x - \tfrac{5}{3}y + 3z = 2,$$
$$x + 2y + 4z = 3?$$

Solution: It must be verified that

$$|4| > |1| + |2|,$$
$$|-5| > |1| + |3|,$$
$$|4| > |1| + |2|.$$

Since these are all true, the Gauss-Seidel method does converge.

A second test for convergence states that either iteration method discussed in this chapter will converge if the coefficient matrix is positive definite. Since this characteristic is very difficult to test, this statement is of doubtful practical value. In the case in which the coefficient matrix, $\mathscr{A}$, is symmetric, that is, where

$$\mathscr{A} = \begin{bmatrix} a_{11} & a_{12} & \cdots & a_{1n} \\ a_{12} & a_{22} & \cdots & a_{2n} \\ \vdots & & & \vdots \\ a_{1n} & a_{2n} & \cdots & a_{nn} \end{bmatrix}, \tag{6.6.16}$$

$\mathscr{A}$ is positive definite if all the determinants

$$|a_{11}|, \begin{vmatrix} a_{11} & a_{12} \\ a_{12} & a_{22} \end{vmatrix}, \begin{vmatrix} a_{11} & a_{12} & a_{13} \\ a_{12} & a_{22} & a_{23} \\ a_{13} & a_{23} & a_{33} \end{vmatrix}, \ldots, \begin{vmatrix} a_{11} & \cdots & a_{1n} \\ \vdots & & \vdots \\ a_{1n} & \cdots & a_{mn} \end{vmatrix} \tag{6.6.17}$$

are positive. But this is not an easy test to apply.

* See for example Theorem 6.2 in John Todd, *A Survey of Numerical Analysis*, McGraw-Hill Book Company, New York, 1962, pp. 224, 225, and Theorem 1.4 in Richard S. Varga, *Matrix Iterative Analysis*, Prentice-Hall Inc., Englewood Cliffs, N.J., 1962, pp. 13, 14.

Problems

6.1 Solve the following system of equations by the Gauss elimination process,

$$0.357x + 0.203y + 0.714z = 0.017,$$
$$-0.206x + 0.295y + 0.371z = 0.111,$$
$$0.412x + 0.315y + 0.604z = 0.149,$$

(a) using pseudo-arithmetic which rounds all results to six decimal places,

(b) rounding each number to two decimal places to begin with and using pseudo-arithmetic which rounds all results to two decimal places,

6.2 Find the inverse of the matrix

$$A = \begin{bmatrix} 0.791 & 0.201 & 0.114 \\ 0.201 & 0.354 & 0.012 \\ 0.114 & 0.012 & -0.910 \end{bmatrix}$$

by the Gauss elimination process. How does round-off error affect your answer?

6.3 A famous "ill-conditioned" matrix, i.e., one which is nearly singular, is the finite dimensional Hilbert matrix, $\mathcal{H}$. If $\mathcal{H}$ is an $n \times n$ matrix, then

$$\mathcal{H} = (h_{ij}),$$

where $h_{ij} = \dfrac{1}{i + j - 1}$, $i, j = 1, 2, \ldots, n$.

(a) Find $\mathcal{H}^{-1}$ for $n = 5$, by Gauss elimination.

(b) If a computer is available, find $\mathcal{H}^{-1}$ by Gauss elimination for $n = 10$.

6.4 Show that the Hilbert matrix does not satisfy the criterion $|a_{ii}| > \Sigma |a_{ij}|$ but that it is positive definite.

6.5 Approximate the solution of

$$\mathcal{H}\mathcal{X} = \mathcal{Y},$$

where $\mathcal{H}$ is a 4×4 Hilbert matrix, $\mathcal{X} = \begin{bmatrix} x_1 \\ x_2 \\ x_3 \\ x_4 \end{bmatrix}$, and $\mathcal{Y} = \begin{bmatrix} 2 \\ 4 \\ 6 \\ 7 \end{bmatrix}$.

6.6 Solve by Gauss elimination the system

$$
\begin{bmatrix}
6 & 2 & 1 & 3 \\
4 & 3 & 2 & -1 \\
7 & -1 & 4 & 4 \\
1 & 5 & 3 & -7
\end{bmatrix}
\begin{bmatrix}
x \\ y \\ z \\ w
\end{bmatrix}
=
\begin{bmatrix}
0 \\ 0 \\ 0 \\ 0
\end{bmatrix}.
$$

6.7 Repeat Problem 6.1, using the Gauss-Seidel iterative method until successive approximations differ by no more than 10^{-3}.

6.8 Repeat Problem 6.1 by the relaxation method, until successive approximations differ by no more than 10^{-3}. That is, if (x_i, y_i, z_i) is the ith approximation, evaluate

$$
\begin{bmatrix}
R_1 \\ R_2 \\ R_3
\end{bmatrix}
=
\begin{bmatrix}
0.357 & 0.203 & 0.714 \\
-0.206 & 0.295 & 0.371 \\
0.412 & -0.315 & 0.604
\end{bmatrix}
\begin{bmatrix}
x_i \\ y_i \\ z_i
\end{bmatrix}
-
\begin{bmatrix}
0.017 \\ 0.111 \\ 0.149
\end{bmatrix}.
$$

Then determine the maximum of $|R_1|$, $|R_2|$, $|R_3|$. If $|R_j|$ is the maximum, solve the jth equation for the jth variable in terms of the other two variables. Using the values of these two variables obtained at the ith iteration, form a new value of the jth variable. This new value, together with the old values of the other two variables becomes the $(i + 1)$st iterate. Repeat this process until the desired accuracy is obtained.

6.9 Repeat Problem 6.1, using the Gauss–Jordan method.

6.10 What are the $\mathscr{F}_i$ matrices of Equation 6.3.6 for Problem 6.1?

6.11 What are the $\mathscr{S}_i$ matrices of Equation 6.3.10 for Problem 6.9?

CHAPTER 7

Least-Squares Polynomial Approximation

THE METHOD of fitting given data by a polynomial which coincides with the data at certain specified points is in some cases a rather inefficient one. In particular, when the function is known at *all* points in an interval, it seems undesirable to select only a relatively small set of arbitrarily chosen points at which to "match". Using a large number of points results in a prohibitively high degree polynomial for numerical computations.

A second situation in which the "matching" method of Chapter 3 is not desirable is the case in which only a discrete set of approximate values are known and in which the degree of reliability of such values is not clearly established, as is often the case for experimental data. A high degree polynomial which "matches" the values given may, in fact, vary widely from the true curve between the match points.

The method of least squares is designed for treatment of these two classes of problems and is the subject of the present chapter. For a more detailed development see Hildebrand,* *Introduction to Numerical Analysis*, Chapter 7.

7.1 The Principle of Least Squares

In place of requiring that an approximating function agree exactly at a restricted number of specified points, it is often preferable to require that the function approximate the given function over a domain, D, as well as possible according to some selected criterion. The least-squares

* Hildebrand, F. B., *Introduction to Numerical Analysis*, McGraw-Hill Book Company, New York, 1957.

"best approximation", attributed to Legendre, requires that the aggregate of the squared errors in D be a minimum. The terms domain and aggregate are defined in the following manner.

Definition 7.1.1 A domain, D, as used in the least-squares development, is either (1) an interval (a, b) or (2) a discrete set of points, in accordance with Definitions 7.1.2 and 7.1.3.

Definition 7.1.2 If the domain, D, is an interval, the aggregate, $\{f(x)\}$, of a function $f(x)$ over D is given by

$$\{f(x)\} = \int_a^b f(x) \, dx. \tag{7.1.1}$$

Definition 7.1.3 If the domain, D, is a discrete set of points,

$$D = \{x_0, x_1, \ldots, x_n\},$$

the aggregate, $\{f(x)\}$, of a function $f(x)$ over D is given by

$$\{f(x)\} = \sum_{i=0}^{n} f(x_i). \tag{7.1.2}$$

Thus the aggregate $\{f(x)\}$ may not exist. In the case of D being an interval, (a, b), $\int_a^b f(x) \, dx$ may not exist, while in the case of D being a discrete set of points $\{x_0, x_1, \ldots, x_n\}$, $f(x_i)$ may not be defined for some x_i in D.

In most of this chapter it is assumed that all values assigned to $f(x)$ are of equal precision although the more general theory allows for a weighting factor or measure of the relative precision of values of $f(x)$ for various values of x.

Suppose exact values of $f(x)$ are known over the domain D and that the approximation sought is to be of the form

$$f(x) \approx \sum_{k=0}^{n} a_k \phi_k(x), \tag{7.1.3}$$

where $\phi_0(x)$, $\phi_1(x)$, $\ldots$, $\phi_n(x)$ are $(n + 1)$ functions to be chosen. In particular, the choice $\phi_0(x) = 1$, $\phi_1(x) = x, \ldots, \phi_n(x) = x^n$ might be made, although other choices of these functions, which lead to polynomials of degree n, are often more convenient. The purpose of the present discussion is to establish a basis for the selection of the $\phi_i(x)$ as well as to determine the coefficients, a_k.

The difference between the *exact* values of $f(x)$ and the approximate values of Equation 7.1.3 is

$$R(x) = f(x) - \sum_{k=0}^{n} a_k \phi_k(x). \tag{7.1.4}$$

According to the least-squares principle, the best approximation will be that for which the aggregate of $R^2(x)$ is a minimum. In order to avoid restricting the present argument to a domain, D, of either a discrete set of points or an interval, the aggregate is symbolized as $\{R^2(x)\}$.

If it is assumed that the $(n + 1)$ functions $\phi_0(x), \ldots, \phi_n(x)$ are given, the coefficients $a_0, \ldots, a_n$ remain to be determined. But then in Equation 7.1.4 for fixed x, only the a_k can be varied so that $\{R^2(x)\}$ should be considered a function of the variables $a_0, a_1, \ldots, a_n$ for the minimization.

From Equation 7.1.4, the aggregate squared error is

$$\{R^2(x)\} = \left\{ \left[f(x) - \sum_{k=0}^{n} a_k \phi_k(x) \right]^2 \right\}. \tag{7.1.5}$$

A necessary condition for x to be a minimum of $\{R^2(x)\}$ is

$$\frac{\partial}{\partial a_r} \left\{ \left[f(x) - \sum_{k=0}^{n} a_k \phi_k(x) \right]^2 \right\} = 0 \qquad (r = 0, 1, \ldots, n) \tag{7.1.6}$$

or

$$\frac{\partial}{\partial a_r} \left\{ (f(x))^2 - 2f(x) \sum_{k=0}^{n} a_k \phi_k(x) + \left(\sum_{0=k}^{n} a_k \phi_k(x) \right)^2 \right\} = 0$$
$$(r = 0, 1, \ldots, n). \tag{7.1.7}$$

Performing the differentiation* symbolized in Equation 7.1.7 gives

$$\left\{ -2f(x)\phi_r(x) + 2\sum_{k=0}^{n} a_k \phi_k(x)\phi_r(x) \right\} = 0 \qquad (r = 0, 1, \ldots, n). \tag{7.1.8}$$

Using the fact that the aggregate of a finite sum is equal to the sum of the aggregates, Equation 7.1.8, becomes

$$\left\{ \sum_{k=0}^{n} a_k \phi_k(x)\phi_r(x) \right\} = \{\phi_r(x) f(x)\} \qquad (r = 0, 1, \ldots, n). \tag{7.1.9}$$

This leads to $(n + 1)$ simultaneous linear equations in the $(n + 1)$ parameters $a_0, a_1, \ldots, a_n$. These equations are called the *normal equations* of the least-squares process.

Exercises

1. Let D be the interval $(0, 1)$, and let $f(x) = e^x$. Moreover, suppose $\phi_0(x) = 1$, $\phi_1(x) = x$, $\phi_2(x) = x^2$, and that it is desired to approximate $f(x)$ over D by $f(x) \approx a_0\phi_0(x) + a_1\phi_1(x) + a_2\phi_2(x)$. Write the expression, using these specific values, which corresponds to Equation 7.1.5.

* If the domain D is a discrete set of points, to pass from Equation 7.1.7 to Equation 7.1.8 requires only that the expression inside the aggregate symbol in Equation 7.1.7 be a differentiable function with respect to $a_0, a_1, \ldots, a_n$. If the domain D is an interval (a, b), then it is sufficient to require that the same expression be a continuous function of x and $a_0, a_1, \ldots, a_n$ and that it be a differentiable function of $a_0, a_1, \ldots, a_n$. Thus in either case, it is sufficient to require that $f(x)$ and the $\phi_k(x)$ be continuous.

2. For Exercise 1 above, derive the set of three equations in a_0, a_1, a_2 corresponding to Equation 7.1.9.

3. Solve the set of equations for a_0, a_1, a_2, in Exercise 2 above. Observe that the coefficient matrix is a finite Hilbert matrix.

4. What is the aggregate squared error of the resulting approximation?

7.2 Least-Squares Approximation over a Domain of a Discrete Set of Points

If the domain, D, over which a "best approximation" is sought, is a discrete set of $m + 1$ points, Equation 7.1.9 takes the form

$$\sum_{i=0}^{m} \sum_{k=0}^{n} a_k \phi_k(x_i) \phi_r(x_i) = \sum_{i=0}^{m} \phi_r(x_i) f(x_i), \qquad r = 0, 1, \ldots, n. \quad (7.2.1)$$

Summing with respect to k on the left side of this last equation gives

$$a_0 \sum_{i=0}^{m} \phi_r(x_i) \phi_0(x_i) + a_1 \sum_{i=0}^{m} \phi_r(x_i) \phi_1(x_i) + \cdots + a_n \sum_{i=0}^{m} \phi_r(x_i) \phi_n(x_i)$$

$$= \sum_{i=0}^{m} \phi_r(x_i) f(x_i), \qquad r = 0, 1, \ldots, n. \quad (7.2.2)$$

Thus, since r takes on the $(n + 1)$ values $0, 1, \ldots, n$, Equation 7.2.2 represents a set of $(n + 1)$ simultaneous linear equations in the $(n + 1)$ parameters $a_0, a_1, \ldots, a_n$. While these equations may appear to be rather complex, careful examination of Equation 7.2.2 reveals that the actual computation of the coefficients in the $(n + 1)$ equations yield rather easily to a tabular method.

An initial tabulation is set up with $(m + 1)$ rows, corresponding to the $(m + 1)$ values of x_i, and $(n + 2)$ columns, corresponding to the functions $\phi_0(x_i)$, $\phi_1(x_i)$, $\cdots$, $\phi_n(x_i)$ and $f(x_i)$, as shown in Table 7.2.1.

This table is the basis from which further tabulations are constructed, one for each value of r. For $r = 0$, each column of Table 7.2.1 is multiplied, term by term, by the corresponding term in the first column.

TABLE 7.2.1

$\phi_0(x_0)$	$\phi_1(x_0)$	$\phi_2(x_0) \cdots \phi_n(x_0)$	$f(x_0)$
$\phi_0(x_1)$	$\phi_1(x_1)$	$\phi_2(x_1) \cdots \phi_n(x_1)$	$f(x_1)$
$\phi_0(x_2)$	$\phi_1(x_2)$	$\phi_2(x_2) \cdots \phi_n(x_2)$	$f(x_2)$
$\vdots$			$\vdots$
$\phi_0(x_m)$	$\phi_1(x_m)$	$\phi_2(x_m) \cdots \phi_n(x_m)$	$f(x_m)$

TABLE 7.2.2

$\phi_0^2(x_0)$	$\phi_0(x_0)\phi_1(x_0)$	$\phi_0(x_0)\phi_2(x_0)$	$\cdots$	$\phi_0(x_0)\phi_n(x_0)$	$\phi_0(x_0)f(x_0)$
$\phi_0^2(x_1)$	$\phi_0(x_1)\phi_1(x_1)$	$\phi_0(x_1)\phi_2(x_1)$	$\cdots$	$\phi_0(x_1)\phi_n(x_1)$	$\phi_0(x_1)f(x_1)$
$\phi_0^2(x_m)$	$\phi_0(x_m)\phi_1(x_m)$	$\phi_0(x_m)\phi_2(x_m)$	$\cdots$	$\phi_0(x_m)\phi_n(x_m)$	$\phi_0(x_m)f(x_m)$

It is readily apparent that summing the successive columns in this last tabulation gives the $(n + 1)$ coefficients on the left side of Equation 7.2.2 and the term on the right side of Equation 7.2.2, for $r = 0$.

Similarly, further tabulations formed from Table 7.2.1, using columns $2, 3, \ldots, n + 1$ successively as the multiplying column, contain columns which sum to the coefficients of the a_k and the constant term in Equation 7.2.2 for $r = 1, 2, \ldots, n$.

One point to be noted particularly in regard to the method of least-squared error is the fact that when the $\phi_i(x)$ are polynomials, the number of points used and the degree of the approximating polynomial are independent. Therefore more points, and hence more pertinent information about the function, can be used without raising the degree of the approximating polynomial.

EXAMPLE 7.2.1.   Find the quadratic equation which gives the best fit in the least-squares sense for the points given in the table.

x	0	1	2	3	4	5
$f(x)$	-5	-3	2	5	7	10

Solution: The requirements of a quadratic, which is written symbolically as $a_0 + a_1x + a_2x^2$, can be met by defining

$$\phi_0(x) = 1, \ \phi_1(x) = x, \ \phi_2(x) = x^2.$$

The initial tabulation (Table 7.2.1) is as follows.

$\phi_0(x)$	$\phi_1(x)$	$\phi_2(x)$	$f(x)$
1	0	0	-5
1	1	1	-3
1	2	4	2
1	3	9	5
1	4	16	7
1	5	25	10
6	15	55	16

this is also the first computing table (Table 7.2.2) because the $\phi_0(x_i)$ are all ones. The sums of the columns give the equation

$$6a_0 + 15a_1 + 55a_2 = 16.$$

The second and third computing tabulations are as follows.

0	0	0	0	0	0	0	0
1	1	1	−3	1	1	1	−3
2	4	8	4	4	8	16	8
3	9	27	15	9	27	81	45
4	16	64	28	16	64	256	116
5	25	125	50	25	125	625	250
15	55	225	94	55	225	979	412

The remaining equations are, therefore,

$$15a_0 + 55a_1 + 225a_2 = 94 \quad \text{and} \quad 55a_0 + 225a_1 + 979a_2 = 412.$$

The solution of these three equations is

$$a_2 = -0.125, \qquad a_1 = 3.711, \qquad a_0 = -5.464$$

and the required quadratic is

$$P_2(x) = -5.464 + 3.711x - 0.125x^2.$$

A check on how good this "best fit" is can be made by computing $P_2(x)$ for the given values of x and comparing with given values of $f(x)$.

x	$f(x)$	$P_2(x)$	$R(x)$	$R^2(x)$
0	−5	−5.464	0.464	0.2153
1	−3	−1.878	−1.122	1.2589
2	2	1.458	0.542	0.2938
3	5	4.544	0.456	0.2079
4	7	7.380	−0.380	0.1444
5	10	9.966	−0.034	0.0012
			$\sum R^2(x) =$	2.1215

The sum of $R^2(x) = 2.1215$ gives less information, perhaps, than an examination of the table in detail. Such an examination shows that one point, $x = 1$, gives a particularly bad fit and that the correspondence is closer at the two ends.

An examination of the original data shows a continuously increasing function and suggests that a straight line might be more apt to fit the data than a parabola. To check this conclusion, the least-squares line, $P_1(x) = a_0 + a_1 x$ can be found by using the first, second and last columns of the first two tables used in computing the quadratic. Thus the tables

1	0	−5		0	0	0
1	1	−3		1	1	−3
1	2	2		2	4	4
1	3	5		3	9	15
1	4	7		4	16	28
1	5	10		5	25	50
6	15	16		15	55	94

give

$$6a_0 + 15a_1 = 16, \qquad 15a_0 + 55a_1 = 94.$$

Solving these two equations gives

$$a_0 = -5.046 \quad \text{and} \quad a_1 = 3.085.$$

Hence

$$P_1(x) = 3.085x - 5.046.$$

The degree of correspondence is shown in the following tabulation.

x	$f(x)$	$P_1(x)$	$R(x)$	$R^2(x)$
0	−5	−5.046	0.046	0.0021
1	−3	−1.961	−1.039	1.0800
2	2	1.124	0.876	0.7674
3	5	4.209	0.791	0.6257
4	7	7.294	−0.294	0.0864
5	10	10.379	−0.379	0.1436
			$\sum R^2(x) =$	2.6852

This tabulation reveals that, in spite of the fact that the data suggests a straight line, the overall fit is better when a parabola is used.

Least-squares polynomial approximation for discrete points is very well adapted for automatic-computer usage. One advantage of this method is that a very large number of initial values may be used without increasing the final storage needed in the computer, since the computation and summing may be done as the initial data is read into the computer. After all data is in the computer, it is necessary only to select the proper sums as coefficients in a set of linear equations.

Finding the final polynomial equation requires the solution of a set of linear equations. Methods for finding such solutions by means of a digital computer are discussed in Chapter 6. Since systems of equations can be difficult to solve numerically, this is one of the disadvantages of the least-squares method. If, after the polynomial is completely determined, any interpolation or extrapolation is required, the problem is simply one of polynomial evaluation.

Exercise

Work Example 7.2.1 over, using

$$\phi_0(x) = 1 + x, \qquad \phi_1(x) = x - x^2, \qquad \phi_2(x) = 1 + x + x^2.$$

How does the approximation $a_0\phi_0(x) + a_1\phi_1(x) + a_2\phi_2(x)$ compare with that obtained in Example 7.2.1?

7.3 Least–Squares Approximation Over an Interval; Orthogonal Polynomials

If the domain, D, is an interval, (a, b), rather than a discrete set of points, the aggregate in Equation 7.1.9 becomes an integral and Equation 7.1.9 is written as

$$\sum_{k=0}^{n} a_k \int_a^b \phi_r(x)\phi_k(x)\, dx = \int_a^b \phi_r(x) f(x)\, dx \qquad (r = 0, 1, \ldots, n). \quad (7.3.1)$$

This last equation can be written as

$$\int_a^b \sum_{k=0}^{n} a_k \phi_r(x)\phi_k(x)\, dx = \int_a^b \phi_r(x) f(x)\, dx \qquad (r = 0, 1, \ldots, n). \quad (7.3.2)$$

For purposes of clarity, let the summation in the left-hand term be expanded. Equation 7.3.2 then becomes

$$\int_a^b a_0\phi_0(x)\phi_r(x)\, dx + \int_a^b a_1\phi_1(x)\phi_r(x)\, dx + \cdots + \int_a^b a_n\phi_n(x)\phi_r(x)\, dx$$

$$= \int_a^b \phi_r(x) f(x)\, dx \qquad (r = 0, 1, \ldots, n). \quad (7.3.3)$$

If now the $\phi_i(x)$ are chosen as *orthogonal polynomials;* i.e., polynomials with the property that

$$\int_a^b \phi_i(x)\phi_j(x)\, dx = 0, \qquad i \neq j, \quad (7.3.4)$$

Equation 7.3.3 reduces to

$$\int_a^b a_r\phi_r^2(x)\, dx = \int_a^b \phi_r(x) f(x)\, dx \qquad (r = 0, 1, \ldots, n) \quad (7.3.5)$$

or

$$a_r = \frac{\displaystyle\int_a^b \phi_r(x) f(x)\, dx}{\displaystyle\int_a^b \phi_r{}^2(x)\, dx}. \qquad (7.3.6)$$

The problem is now reduced to one of choosing $\phi_i(x)$ which satisfy Equation 7.3.4 and at the same time give a satisfactory fit for the particular problem at hand.

There are a number of sets of orthogonal polynomials which have been derived to fit the requirements of Equation 7.3.4. The scope and size of this book do not allow for a discussion of all, or even several, of these sets of polynomials. Hence only two sets are discussed rather briefly, not because they are necessarily the best but because they are commonly used ones and serve to illustrate how such polynomials are used, which is all that is attempted here.

Since the mathematics involved in arriving at a set of orthogonal polynomials is outside the scope of this book, more because of quantity than because of difficulty, the selected polynomials will be given, with little or no theoretical background, and applied to a particular problem by way of illustration.

Exercises

1. Show that $\sin x$ and $\cos x$ are orthogonal on the interval $(0, \pi)$ but not on the interval $(0, \pi/2)$.

2. For what values of b are x and $1 - x$ orthogonal over the interval $(0, b)$?

7.4 Legendre Approximation

For the set of orthogonal polynomials called the *Legendre polynomials,* which apply over an interval of finite length, it is first assumed that a linear change of variable has been made to transform the given interval (a, b) into the interval* $(-1, 1)$. The rth Legendre polynomial, $L_r(x)$, is defined as

$$L_r(x) = \frac{1}{2^r r!} \frac{d^r}{dx^r} (x^2 - 1)^r. \qquad (7.4.1)$$

---

* To change the interval of integration from (a, b) to $(-1, 1)$ one can make the substitution $x = [u(b - a) + a + b]/2$ in $\int_a^b f(x)\, dx$ to obtain $\int_1^1 q(u)\, du.$

The requirement that the polynomials $L_r(x)$ be orthogonal is more than met. The way the $L_r(x)$ are derived is to determine all those polynomials $L_r(x)$ which are orthogonal to *every* polynomial $Q_{r-1}(x)$ of degree $r - 1$ or less. As a result, not only is

$$\int_{-1}^{1} L_r(x)L_s(x)\, dx = 0 \qquad (r \neq s) \tag{7.4.2}$$

satisfied, but also

$$\int_{-1}^{1} L_r(x)Q_{r-1}(x)\, dx = 0 \tag{7.4.3}$$

is satisfied for any polynomial $Q_{r-1}(x)$ of degree $r - 1$ or less.

Evaluation of Equation 7.4.1 for $r = 0, 1, 2$ and 3 gives the polynomials

$$L_0(x) = 1, \qquad L_1(x) = x, \qquad L_2(x) = \tfrac{1}{2}(3x^2 - 1),$$
$$L_3(x) = \tfrac{1}{2}(5x^3 - 3x). \tag{7.4.4}$$

Additional polynomials may be obtained either by using Equation 7.4.1 (see Problem 7.9) or by use of the recurrence formula

$$L_{r+1}(x) = \frac{2r + 1}{r + 1}\, x\, L_r(x) - \frac{r}{r + 1}\, L_{r-1}(x). \tag{7.4.5}$$

In order to apply the Legendre polynomials, it is necessary to evaluate the expression

$$a_r = \frac{\displaystyle\int_{-1}^{1} L_r(x)\,f(x)\, dx}{\displaystyle\int_{-1}^{1} L_r^{\,2}(x)\, dx}, \tag{7.4.6}$$

which is the form Equation 7.3.6 assumes for Legendre polynomials. It is possible but somewhat involved, mathematically, to show that Equation 7.4.6 actually takes the very simple form of

$$a_r = (2r + 1)/2 \int_{-1}^{1} f(x)L_r(x)\, dx. \tag{7.4.7}$$

Hence to apply the Legendre polynomials to a particular problem it is necessary only to evaluate Equation 7.4.7 for as many values of r as desired and thus determine the approximating polynomial

$$P_m(x) = a_0 + a_1 L_1(x) + a_2 L_2(x) + a_3 L_3(x) + \cdots + a_m L_m(x). \tag{7.4.8}$$

Since the coefficients of the polynomials in Equation 7.4.8 involve an integration, use of this method on a computer hinges on numerical integration, which is discussed in Chapter 4. Once the a_i in Equation 7.4.8 are obtained, the pertinent Legendre polynomials must be supplied and coefficients of corresponding powers of x may be combined. If the polynomial itself is the final goal, this combination can perhaps be done by hand as easily as in the computer and the computer problem becomes one merely of numerical integration. If, however, the polynomial is to be used for interpolation or other evaluation, either the combining of like powers of x must be done in the machine, also, or a second entry to the computer made with the new information, i.e., the polynomial coefficients.

EXAMPLE 7.4.1   Find the Legendre least-squares approximation of degree four,

$$P_4(x) = a_0 L_0(x) + a_1 L_1(x) + a_2 L_2(x) + a_3 L_3(x) + a_4 L_4(x),$$

to $f(x) = e^{-x}$.

Solution: The terms to be evaluated are given by Equation 7.4.7 for $= 0, 1, 2, 3$ and 4.

$$a_0 = \frac{1}{2} \int_{-1}^{1} f(x)\, L_0(x)\, dx = \frac{1}{2} \int_{-1}^{+1} e^{-x}\, dx = -\frac{1}{2} e^{-x} \Big|_{-1}^{1} = 1.175201.$$

$$a_1 = \frac{2+1}{2} \int_{-1}^{1} f(x)\, L_1(x)\, dx = \frac{3}{2} \int_{-1}^{1} x e^{-x}\, dx = \frac{3}{2} \Big[-x e^{-x} - e^{-x} \Big]_{-1}^{+1}$$
$$= -1.103638.$$

$$a_2 = \frac{2(2)+1}{2} \int_{-1}^{1} f(x)\, L_2(x)\, dx = \frac{5}{2} \int_{-1}^{1} \frac{1}{2}(3x^2 - 1) e^{-x}\, dx$$
$$= \frac{5}{4} \Big[3[-x^2 e^{-x} - 2x e^{-x} - 2 e^{-x}] + e^{-x} \Big]_{-1}^{1} = 0.357814.$$

$$a_3 = \frac{2(3)+1}{2} \int_{-1}^{1} f(x)\, L_3(x)\, dx = \frac{7}{2} \int_{-1}^{1} \frac{1}{2}(5x^3 - 3x) e^{-x}\, dx$$
$$= \frac{7}{4} \Big[-5x^3 e^{-x} - 15x^2 e^{-x} - 27x e^{-x} - 27 e^{-x} \Big]_{-1}^{+1} = -0.070455.$$

$$a_4 = \frac{2(4)+1}{2} \int_{-1}^{1} f(x)\, L_4(x)\, dx = \frac{9}{2} \int_{-1}^{1} \tfrac{1}{8}(35x^4 - 30x^2 + 3) e^{-x}\, dx$$
$$= \frac{9}{16} \Big[[-35x^4 - 140x^3 - 390x^2 - 780x - 783] e^{-x} \Big]_{-1}^{1}$$
$$= +0.009967.$$

$$f(x) = e^{-x} \approx P_4(x)$$

$$= 1.175201 - 1.103638x + \frac{0.357814}{2}(3x^2 - 1)$$

$$- \frac{0.070455}{2}(5x^3 - 3x) + \frac{0.009967}{8}(35x^4 - 30x^2 + 3)$$

$$= 1.0 - 0.9979x + 0.4993x^2 - 0.1761x^3 + 0.0436x^4.$$

As a check on the accuracy of this approximating polynomial, $e^{-0.1}$ as computed by $P_4(x)$ is 0.90503. A four-place table gives $e^{-0.1}$ as 0.9048. If only the first four terms of the polynomial are used, that is $P_3(x)$, the computed value of $e^{-0.1}$ is 0.90169 and if six terms are included, that is, $P_5(x)$, the value is 0.09486. This gives some indication of the rate of convergence.

It is interesting to note that it is necessary to start with values of e and e^{-1} to eight decimal places to obtain answers accurate to four places.

Exercises

1. Convert the range of integration of $\int_0^4 \frac{1}{2} \sin \frac{x-2}{2} dx$ to the range $(-1, 1)$.

2. Approximate $\frac{1}{2} \sin \frac{x-2}{2}$ on the interval $(0, 4)$ by $a_0 + a_1 L_1(x)$. Determine a_0 and a_1.

7.5 Another Orthogonal Polynomial Approximation

As noted in an earlier section, there are many sets of orthogonal polynomials which are derived by imposing various restrictions, by various changes of variables or by assigning various weighting factors. These polynomials may be used in Equation 7.3.5 to form a polynomial approximation to $f(x)$ on the range $(-1, 1)$.

One of these sets of polynomials which is sometimes encountered in engineering literature, particularly in electrical network synthesis, is called Chebychev (or Tschebycheff) approximation. Since even a "speaking acquaintance" is probably better than none at all, the formulas for two of the several Chebychev approximations are given here.

The first four of the Chebychev polynomials are

$$T_0(x) = 1, \qquad T_1(x) = x, \qquad T_2(x) = 2x^2 - 1, \qquad T_3(x) = 4x^3 - 3x,$$

$$\tag{7.5.1}$$

and the recurrence formula is

$$T_{r+1}(x) = 2xT_r(x) - T_{r-1}(x). \tag{7.5.2}$$

Equations for the rth coefficient in the equation

$$y(x) = \sum_{r=0}^{n} a_r T_r(x) \approx f(x), \qquad -1 < x < 1, \tag{7.5.3}$$

are

$$a_0 = \frac{1}{\pi} \int_{-1}^{1} \frac{f(x)}{\sqrt{1 - x^2}} dx$$

and

$$a_r = \frac{2}{\pi} \int_{-1}^{1} \frac{f(x)T_r(x)}{\sqrt{1 - x^2}} dx, \qquad r \neq 0. \tag{7.5.4}$$

In this case, the polynomial $y(x)$ of Equation 7.5.3 has the property that of all polynomials of degree n or less, the integrated weighted square error

$$E_w{}^2 = \int_{-1}^{1} \frac{1}{\sqrt{1 - x^2}} [f(x) - y_n(x)]^2 \, dx \qquad (7.5.5)$$

is least when $y_n(x)$ is the polynomial of Equation 7.5.3.

If the polynomial $y(x)$ is defined as

$$y(x) = \frac{1}{\sqrt{1 - x^2}} \sum_{r=0}^{n} b_r T_r(x) \approx f(x), \qquad -1 < x < 1, \qquad (7.5.6)$$

the coefficients are defined as

$$b_0 = \frac{1}{\pi} \int_{-1}^{1} f(x) \, dx$$

and

$$b_r = \frac{2}{\pi} \int_{-1}^{1} f(x) \, T_r(x) \, dx, \qquad r \neq 0. \qquad (7.5.7)$$

The polynomial $y(x)$ of Equation 7.5.6 is now such that the integrated weighted square error

$$E_w{}^2 = \int_{-1}^{1} \sqrt{1 - x^2} \, [f(x) - y_n(x)]^2 \, dx \qquad (7.5.8)$$

is a minimum when $y_n(x)$ is the $y(x)$ of Equation 7.5.6.

For a detailed discussion of other sets of orthogonal polynomials, for example, the Laguerre approximations and the Hermite approximations, the reader is referred to Hildebrand, *Introduction to Numerical Analysis*, pages 275 to 283.

Exercises

1. Find $T_4(x)$ by the formula in Equation 7.5.2.

2. Approximate $\sin x$ by $y(x)$ as given in Equation 7.5.6, with $n = 1$. Evaluate Equation 7.5.8 for the resulting $y(x)$.

3. Let $\sin x$ be approximated by $z(x) = x$. Evaluate Equation 7.5.8 in this case and compare the result with that obtained in Exercise 2 above.

Problems

7.1 Write the equations from Equation 7.2.2 for $r = 0, 1,$ and 2 in detail and show the tabulations described in Section 7.2 to lead to the coefficients of a_0, a_1, and a_2.

7.2   Fit a straight line to the given set of points by the least-squares method. Plot the points and the resulting line. Also compute the squared deviations and the sum of these deviations.

x	0	1	2	3	4	5
$f(x)$	-5	-1	1	2	4	10

7.3   Repeat Problem 7.2 but with a second-degree polynomial.
7.4   Repeat Problem 7.2 for the following table of values.

x	0	1	2	3	4	5
$f(x)$	-3	$+1$	$+4$	-1	-3	$+2$

7.5   Repeat Problem 7.4 for the values in Problem 7.4.
7.6   Find the first four coefficients of the Legendre approximation for e^x. Write the polynomial and use this polynomial to evaluate $e^{0.01}$ and $e^{0.2}$.
7.7   Find the first four coefficients of the Legendre approximation for xe^x. Write the polynomial and use this polynomial to evaluate xe^x for $x = 0.1$.
7.8   Use Equation 7.4.1 to find the polynomials in Equation 7.4.4.
7.9   Use Equation 7.4.1 to find $L_4(x)$ and $L_5(x)$.
7.10   Use Equation 7.4.5 to find $L_4(x)$ and $L_5(x)$. Compare with the results of Problem 7.9.

CHAPTER 8

Gaussian Quadrature

IN CHAPTER 4 numerical integration was discussed, using the Gregory-Newton interpolation polynomial and equally spaced abscissas. Corresponding formulas of comparable accuracy are possible when the spacing on the abscissa is not so restricted but is instead optimally determined.

Since formulas of this latter type usually involve irrational numbers, both as abscissas and as, in some cases, weighting functions, such formulas are not convenient for hand calculations. With use of digital computers, however, this irrationality is of little significance and is outweighed by the advantage of the fewer ordinates required for comparable accuracy. This is particularly true if the ordinates needed are difficult to obtain.

In general, in the formulas of the Newton-Cotes type, discussed in Chapter 4, the integral $\int_a^b f(x)\,dx$ is written as

$$\int_a^b fx)\,dx = \int_a^b P_m(x)\,dx + \int_a^b R_m(x)\,dx, \qquad (8.1)$$

where $P_m(x)$ is the Gregory-Newton polynomial of degree m and $R_m(x)$ is the corresponding error term. In the formulas developed in the present chapter, usually called Gaussian quadrature formulas, the integral to be evaluated is $\int_a^b w(x)f(x)\,dx$, where $w(x)$ is a weighting function selected so as to produce particularly simple formulas. As with the Newton-Cotes formulas, $\int_a^b w(x)f(x)\,dx$ is rewritten. This rewritten form is

$$\int_a^b w(x)f(x)\,dx = \int_a^b w(x)\,P_{2m-1}(x)\,dx + \int_a^b R_{2m-1}(x)\,dx, \qquad (8.2)$$

where $w(x)$ is a weighting function and $P_{2m-1}(x)$ is one of the least-squares polynomials discussed in Chapter 7.

The derivation of the Gaussian quadrature formulas, and particularly of the error terms associated with these formulas, requires interpolation formulas that make use of ordinates rather than differences of ordinates and that do not depend on equally spaced abscissas. Since such interpolation formulas are not included in the discussion in Chapter 4, the first two sections of this chapter are concerned with the development of two such interpolation formulas.

8.1 Lagrange Interpolation

One interpolation formula which makes use of unequally spaced abscissas is called the Lagrangian interpolation formula.

A function $f(x)$ is to be approximated by a function $y(x)$ defined by

$$y(x) = \sum_{i=0}^{m-1} f(x_i)\, g_i(x), \tag{8.1.1}$$

where the $g_i(x)$ are to be defined in such a way that

$$y(x_i) = f(x_i). \tag{8.1.2}$$

for $i = 0, 1, \ldots, m - 1$.

Since the functions $g_0(x), g_1(x), \ldots, g_{m-1}(x)$ are to be selected subject so far only to the restriction in Equation 8.1.2, it is convenient to require that

$$g_i(x_k) = 0, \qquad i \neq k,$$
$$g_i(x_i) = 1 \tag{8.1.3}$$

for $i, k = 0, 1, 2, \ldots, m - 1$.

Consider the functions defined by

$$\pi(x) = (x - x_0)(x - x_1) \cdots (x - x_{m-1}) \tag{8.1.4}$$

and

$$l_i(x) = \frac{\pi(x)}{(x - x_i)\pi'(x_i)}, \tag{8.1.5}$$

$$= \frac{(x - x_0)(x - x_1) \cdots (x - x_{i-1})(x - x_{i+1}) \cdots (x - x_{m-1})}{(x_i - x_0)(x_i - x_1) \cdots (x_i - x_{i-1})(x_i - x_{i+1}) \cdots (x_i - x_{m-1})},$$
$$i = 0, 1, \ldots, m - 1 \tag{8.1.6}$$

where, as usual, $\pi'(x_i)$ denotes the derivative of $\pi(x)$ evaluated at x_i. Since for $k \neq i$, Equation 8.1.5 becomes

$$l_i(x_k) = \frac{(x_k - x_0)(x_k - x_1) \cdots (x_k - x_k) \cdots (x_k - x_{m-1})}{(x_k - x_i)\pi'(x_i)}, \tag{8.1.7}$$

then

$$l_i(x_k) = 0 \qquad k \neq i, \tag{8.1.8}$$

whereas from Equation 8.1.6, $l_i(x_k) = 1, \qquad k = i.$

Thus the functions $l_i(x)$ satisfy the requirement of Equation 8.1.3. If, then, $g_i(x) = l_i(x)$, Equation 8.1.1 can be written as

$$y(x) = \sum_{i=0}^{m-1} f(x_i) l_i(x). \tag{8.1.9}$$

The function $y(x)$ is a polynomial of degree $m - 1$ which passes through the m points: $(x_0, f(x_0))(x_1, f(x_1)) \cdots (x_{m-1}, f(x_{m-1}))$.

The remainder term,

$$R_{m-1}(x) = f(x) - y(x), \tag{8.1.10}$$

can be derived in exactly the same way as that for the Gregory-Newton formula (see Section 3.5) and is

$$R_{m-1}(x) = f^{(m)}(\zeta) \frac{(x - x_0)(x - x_1) \cdots (x - x_{m-1})}{m!} = f^{(m)}(\zeta) \frac{\pi(x)}{m!}, \tag{8.1.11}$$

where ζ lies between x_0, x_{m-1}, and x. Finally, solving Equation 8.1.10 for $f(x)$ gives

$$f(x) = y(x) + f^{(m)}(\zeta) \frac{\pi(x)}{m} \tag{8.1.12}$$

or

$$f(x) = \sum_{i=0}^{m-1} f(x_i) l_i(x) + f^{(m)}(\zeta) \frac{\pi(x)}{m!}. \tag{8.1.13}$$

In order to help visualize more clearly the implications of Equation 8.1.9 in terms of actual use, consider this equation in expanded form; i.e.,

$$y(x) = f(x_0) \frac{(x - x_1)(x - x_2) \cdots (x - x_{m-1})}{(x_0 - x_1)(x_0 - x_2) \cdots (x_0 - x_{m-1})},$$

$$+ f(x_1) \frac{(x - x_0)(x - x_2) \cdots (x - x_{m-1})}{(x_1 - x_0)(x_1 - x_2) \cdots (x_1 - x_{m-1})} + \cdots \tag{8.1.14}$$

$$+ f(x_{m-1}) \frac{(x - x_0)(x - x_1) \cdots (x - x_{m-2})}{(x_{m-1} - x_0)(x_{m-1} - x_1) \cdots (x_{m-1} - x_{m-2})}.$$

That this formula requires considerable numerical computation is evident. However, when a digital computer is used, the work of programming is perhaps even less than that required for the Gregory-Newton formula, particularly since the ordinates are used directly and neither difference tables nor factorial polynomials are required.

EXAMPLE 8.1.1   Find log 37, using the abscissas 25, 30, 36, 40, 45, 48.

Solution: From a table of logarithms,

log 25 = 1.39794;   log 30 = 1.47712;   log 36 = 1.55630;

log 40 = 1.60206;   log 45 = 1.65321;   log 48 = 1.68124.

By Equation 8.1.13

$$\log 37 = \sum_{i=0}^{5} \log(x_i) l_i(37) + R_5(37)$$

$$= \log 25 \left[\frac{(37 - 30)(37 - 36)(37 - 40)(37 - 45)(37 - 48)}{(25 - 30)(25 - 36)(25 - 40)(25 - 45)(25 - 48)} \right]$$

$$+ \log 30 \left[\frac{(37 - 25)(37 - 36)(37 - 40)(37 - 45)(37 - 48)}{(30 - 25)(30 - 36)(30 - 40)(30 - 45)(30 - 48)} \right]$$

$$+ \log 36 \left[\frac{(37 - 25)(37 - 30)(37 - 40)(37 - 45)(37 - 48)}{(36 - 25)(36 - 30)(36 - 40)(36 - 45)(36 - 48)} \right]$$

$$+ \log 40 \left[\frac{(37 - 25)(37 - 30)(37 - 36)(37 - 45)(37 - 48)}{(40 - 25)(40 - 30)(40 - 36)(40 - 45)(40 - 48)} \right]$$

$$+ \log 45 \left[\frac{(37 - 25)(37 - 30)(37 - 36)(37 - 40)(37 - 48)}{(45 - 25)(45 - 30)(45 - 36)(45 - 40)(45 - 48)} \right]$$

$$+ \log 48 \left[\frac{(37 - 25)(37 - 30)(37 - 36)(37 - 40)(37 - 45)}{(48 - 25)(48 - 30)(48 - 36)(48 - 40)(48 - 45)} \right]$$

$$+ R_5(37)$$

or

$$\log 37 = 1.39794 \left[\frac{(7)(1)(-3)(-8)(-11)}{(-5)(-11)(-15)(-20)(-23)} \right]$$

$$+ 1.47712 \left[\frac{(12)(1)(-3)(-8)(-11)}{(5)(-6)(-10)(-15)(-18)} \right]$$

$$+ 1.55630 \left[\frac{(12)(7)(-3)(-8)(-11)}{(11)(6)(-4)(-9)(-12)} \right]$$

$$+ 1.60206 \left[\frac{(12)(7)(1)(-8)(-11)}{(15)(10)(4)(-5)(-8)} \right]$$

$$+ 1.65321 \left[\frac{(12)(7)(1)(-3)(-11)}{(20)(15)(9)(5)(-3)} \right]$$

$$+ 1.68124 \left[\frac{(12)(7)(1)(-3)(-8)}{(23)(18)(12)(8)(3)} \right] + R_5(37)$$

$$= 1.39794 \left(\frac{14}{2875} \right) + 1.47712 \left(\frac{-44}{1125} \right) + 1.55630 \left(\frac{7}{9} \right)$$

$$+ 1.60206 \left(\frac{77}{250} \right) + 1.65321 \left(\frac{-77}{1125} \right) + 1.68124 \left(\frac{7}{414} \right) + R_5(37)$$

$$= 0.00681 - 0.05777 + 1.21046 + 0.49343 - 0.11315$$

$$+ 0.02843 + R_5(37)$$

$$= 1.56821 + R_5(37).$$

The answer given in five-place log tables is 1.56820. The difference in the fifth decimal place is to be expected since original values are from five-place log tables.

EXAMPLE 8.1.2   Evaluate the remainder term $R_5(37)$ of Example 8.1.1.

Solution: Using Equation 8.1.11 for the problem in Example 8.1.1 gives

$R_{m-1}(37)$

$$= f^{(6)}(\zeta)\frac{(37-25)(37-30)(37-36)(37-40)(37-45)(37-48)}{6!}$$

$$= -30.8f^{(6)}(\zeta).$$

But

$$f(x) = \log x$$

and

$$\frac{d^n}{dx^n}\log x = \log_{10} e\left(\frac{(-1)^{n-1}(n-1)!}{x^n}\right).$$

Then, since $n = 6$,

$$f^{(6)}(\zeta) = \frac{-0.43429 \times 5!}{\zeta^6} = \frac{-52.1148}{\zeta^6}.$$

In this case $30 < \zeta < 48$ and

$$1.3 \times 10^{-7} < |R_{m-1}(37)| < 2.2 \times 10^{-6}.$$

Exercises

1. Write out Equations 8.1.4, 8.1.5, and 8.1.6 for $m = 2$. Evaluate $l_0(x_0)$, $l_0(x_1)$, $l_1(x_0)$, $l_1(x_1)$.

2. Let $x_0 = 1$, $x_1 = 3$, and $f(x) = 4x + 5$. Make use of the results obtained in Exercise 1 above to write out the approximation to $f(x)$ given by Equation 8.1.9.

3. Evaluate the remainder term for Exercise 2 above as given by Equation 8.1.11 for $x = 2$.

4. For the case $m = 3$, Equation 8.1.1 becomes

$$f(x_0) = y(x_0) = f(x_0)g_0(x_0) + f(x_1)g_1(x_0) + f(x_2)g_2(x_0),$$
$$f(x_1) = y(x_1) = f(x_0)g_0(x_1) + f(x_1)g_1(x_1) + f(x_2)g_2(x_1),$$
$$f(x_2) = y(x_2) = f(x_0)g_0(x_2) + f(x_1)g_1(x_2) + f(x_2)g_2(x_2).$$

These equations can be reduced to matrix form as

$$\mathscr{F} = \mathscr{G}\mathscr{F},$$

where

$$\mathscr{F} = \begin{bmatrix} f(x_0) \\ f(x_1) \\ f(x_2) \end{bmatrix},$$

$$\mathscr{G} = \begin{bmatrix} g_0(x_0)g_1(x_0)g_2(x_0) \\ g_0(x_1)g_1(x_1)g_2(x_1) \\ g_0(x_2)g_1(x_2)g_2(x_2) \end{bmatrix}.$$

The restrictions given in Equation 8.1.3 force $\mathscr{G}$ to be the identity matrix. Can the requirements in Equation 8.1.2 be satisfied if $\mathscr{G}$ is not the identity matrix?

8.2 Hermite Interpolation

The interpolation formulas considered thus far in this book have employed values of the function $f(x)$ alone. In some cases, values of both a function, $f(x)$, and its derivative, $f'(x)$, are available at m points, It is, in such cases, possible to determine a polynomial, $P_{2m-1}(x)$, of degree $2m - 1$, using these $2m$ values. The Hermite interpolation formula is a formula which makes use of these $2m$ values and thus is a formula of degree $2m - 1$ rather than $m - 1$.

The Hermite interpolation formula has the even more important property that its use leads to numerical integration formulas which, while of degree $2m - 1$, do not depend on knowledge of the values of $f'(x)$. It is because of this property that this formula is included in this chapter.

One way to use the $2m$ values, $f(x_i)$ and $f'(x_i)$, $i = 0, \ldots, m - 1$, would be to find a polynomial $P_{2m-1}(x)$ such that

$$f(x) = P_{2m-1}(x) + R_{2m-1}(x), \tag{8.2.1}$$

where

$$P_{2m-1}(x_i) = f(x_i), \qquad i = 0, 1, \ldots, m - 1, \tag{8.2.2}$$

and

$$P'_{2m-1}(x_i) = f'(x_i), \qquad i = 0, 1, \ldots, m - 1. \tag{8.2.3}$$

To find a polynomial $P_{2m-1}(x)$ which satisfies these requirements, first let $P_{2m-1}(x)$ be defined by

$$P_{2m-1}(x) = \sum_{k=0}^{m-1} h_k(x)f(x_k) + \sum_{k=0}^{m-1} \bar{h}_k(x)f'(x_k), \qquad k = 0, 1, \ldots, m - 1, \tag{8.2.4}$$

where $h_k(x)$ and $\bar{h}_k(x)$ are polynomials of degree $2m - 1$.

In order to satisfy the conditions of Equation 8.2.2 it is sufficient that

$$h_k(x_i) = 0, \quad i \neq k,$$
$$h_k(x_i) = 1, \quad i = k,$$

and (8.2.5)

$$\bar{h}_k(x_i) = 0 \quad \text{for all } i.$$

In addition, to satisfy the conditions of Equation 8.2.3 it is sufficient that

$$\bar{h}'_k(x_i) = 0, \quad i \neq k,$$
$$\bar{h}'_k(x_i) = 1, \quad i = k,$$

and (8.2.6)

$$h'_k(x_i) = 0 \quad \text{for all } i.$$

The polynomial $l_i(x)$ of Equation 8.1.6 is a polynomial of degree $m - 1$ with the property that $l_i(x_k) = 0$ for $i \neq k$ and $l_i(x_i) = 1$. Hence the function defined by

$$H_k(x) = [l_k(x)]^2 = \left[\frac{\pi(x)}{(x - x_k)\,\pi'(x_k)} \right]^2 \tag{8.2.7}$$

is a polynomial of degree $2m - 2$, and its derivative is

$$H'_k(x) = \frac{d}{dx}\,[l_k(x)]^2 = 2l_k(x)l'_k(x). \tag{8.2.8}$$

$H_k(x)$ and $H'_k(x)$ have the properties

$$H_k(x_i) = 0, \quad i \neq k,$$
$$H_k(x_i) = 1, \quad i = k,$$
$$H'_k(x_i) = 0, \quad i \neq k,$$
$$H'_k(x_i) = 2l'_i(x_i), \quad i = k. \tag{8.2.9}$$

If now the functions $h_k(x)$ and $\bar{h}_k(x)$ are defined by

$$h_k(x) = r_k(x)H_k(x),$$
$$\bar{h}_k(x) = s_k(x)H_k(x), \tag{8.2.10}$$

where $r_k(x)$ and $s_k(x)$ are linear functions of x, the functions $h_k(x)$ and $\bar{h}_k(x)$ are polynomials of degree $2m - 1$ and can be determined so as to satisfy the conditions of Equations 8.2.5 and 8.2.6 by proper selection of $r_k(x)$ and $s_k(x)$.

Comparison of the conditions of Equations 8.2.5 and 8.2.6 and those of Equation 8.2.9 shows that sufficient conditions on $r_k(x)$ and $s_k(x)$ for

Equations 8.2.5 and 8.2.6 to be satisfied are

$$r_k(x_k) = 1,$$
$$r'_k(x_k) + 2l'_k(x_k) = 0,$$
(8.2.11)

and

$$s_k(x_k) = 0, \qquad s'_k(x_k) = 1.$$
(8.2.12)

These conditions are satisfied if $r_k(x)$ and $s_k(x)$ are defined as

$$r_k(x) = 1 - 2l'_k(x_k)(x - x_k), \qquad s_k(x) = x - x_k.$$
(8.2.13)

The functions $h_k(x)$ and $\bar{h}_k(x)$ are now completely defined as

$$h_k(x) = [1 - 2l'_k(x_k)(x - x_k)][l_k(x)]^2,$$
$$\bar{h}_k(x) = (x - x_k)[l_k(x)]^2,$$
(8.2.14)

and Equation 8.2.1 can be written as

$$f(x) = \sum_{k=0}^{m-1} [1 - 2l'_k(x_k)(x - x_k)][l_k(x)]^2 f(x_k) + \sum_{k=0}^{m-1} (x - x_k)[l_k(x)]^2 f'(x_k)$$
$$+ R_{2m-1}(x).$$
(8.2.15)

This is the Hermite interpolation formula.

The error term $R_{2m-1}(x)$ is derived in the same way as the error term for the Gregory-Newton and Lagrange formulas (see Section 3.5) and is

$$R_{2m-1}(x) = \frac{f^{(2m)}(\zeta)[\pi(x)]^2}{(2m)!},$$
(8.2.16)

where ζ lies in the interval determined by $x, x_0, x_1, \ldots, x_{m-1}$.

The Hermite interpolation formula is, as the introductory paragraph of this section indicates, of importance theoretically as the basis for deriving useful quadrature formulas. As a formula for numerical interpolation, it is a formula which will give a high degree of accuracy with relatively few abscissas and is applicable when both ordinates and their derivatives are known, or can be found.

EXAMPLE 8.2.1 Use the Hermite interpolation formula to find log 13, using log 2, log 3, log 5.

Solution: Let $x_0 = 10$, $x_1 = 12$, and $x_2 = 15$. Then the values of $f(x_i)$ are

$$f(x_0) = \log 10 = 1,$$
$$f(x_1) = \log 12 = \log 3 + 2 \log 2 = 1.07918,$$
$$f(x_1) = \log 15 = \log 3 + \log 5 = 1.17609.$$

To determine the values of $f'(x_i)$ use

$$\frac{d}{dx} \log x = \frac{\log_{10} e}{x} = \frac{0.43429}{x}.$$

Then

$$f'(10) = 0.043429, \quad f'(12) = 0.03619, \quad f'(15) = 0.02895.$$

The values of $l_i(x)$ are found as

$$l_0(x) = l_0(13) = \frac{(13 - 12)(13 - 15)}{(10 - 12)(10 - 15)} = -\frac{1}{5},$$

and in a similar way

$$l_1(13) = 1 \quad \text{and} \quad l_2(13) = \tfrac{1}{5}.$$

It is necessary to evaluate the quantities $l'_i(x_i)$. To this end, examine the function $l'_i(x)$. For this particular problem

$$l_i(x) = \frac{(x - x_j)(x - x_k)}{(x_i - x_j)(x_i - x_k)}, \quad l'_i(x) = \frac{2x - (x_j + x_k)}{(x_i - x_j)(x_i - x_k)},$$

and

$$l'_i(x_i) = \frac{2x_i - (x_j + x_k)}{(x_i - x_j)(x_i - x_k)} = \frac{1}{x_i - x_j} + \frac{1}{x_i - x_k}.$$

In particular, then,

$$l'_0(x_0) = \frac{1}{-2} + \frac{1}{-5} = \frac{-7}{10},$$

$$l'_1(x_1) = \frac{1}{2} + \frac{1}{-3} = \frac{1}{6},$$

$$l'_2(x_2) = \frac{1}{5} + \frac{1}{3} = \frac{8}{15}.$$

To determine $\log 13$,

$$\log 13 = \sum_{i=0}^{2} [1 - 2l'_k(x_i)(13 - x_i)][l_i(x_i)]^2 f(x_i)$$

$$+ \sum_{i=0}^{2} (13 - x_i)[l_i(x)]^2 f'(x_i) + R_5(13)$$

$$= [1 - 2(-.7)(3)](\tfrac{1}{5})^2(1) + [1 - 2(\tfrac{1}{6})(1)](1)^2(1.07918)$$

$$+ [1 - 2(\tfrac{8}{15})(-2)](\tfrac{1}{5})^2(1.17609) + 3(-\tfrac{1}{5})^2(0.043429)$$

$$+ (1)(1)(0.03619) + (-2)(\tfrac{1}{5})^2(0.02895) + R_5(13)$$

$$= 0.2080 + 0.719453 + 0.147403 + 0.005211 + 0.03619$$

$$- 0.002316 + R_5(13) = 1.113941 + R_5(13).$$

The value of log 13 in a five-place log table is 1.11394. The error term for this problem is

$$R_5(x) = \frac{f^{(6)}(\zeta)}{6!} [\pi(x)]^2.$$

Since $[\pi(13)]^2 = 36$ and

$$\frac{d^6 \log x}{dx^6} = \frac{-5!}{x^6}, \qquad \text{then} \qquad R_5(13) = \frac{-6}{\zeta^6}.$$

Since ζ is in the interval determined by x_0, x_1, x_2 and 13, then $10 \leq \zeta \leq 15$, so that $10^6 \leq \zeta^6 \leq 15^6$ and $15^{-6} \leq \dfrac{1}{\zeta^6} \leq 10^{-6}$. Hence

$$|R_5(13)| \leq 6 \times 10^{-6},$$

which agrees well with the accuracy actually obtained.

The following example illustrates the fact that, although the abscissas need not be equally spaced for use of Hermite interpolation, such equal spacing can be used.

EXAMPLE 8.2.2.   Given the following table of values.

x	$f(x)$	$f'(x)$
0.4	0.3894	0.9211
0.5	0.4794	0.8776
0.6	0.5646	0.8253

Use the Hermite interpolation formula to find $f(0.55)$. What can be said about the error term?

Solution: The values of $[l_i(x)]^2$ and $l'_i(x_i)$ are computed as

$$[l_0(x)]^2 = \left[\frac{(0.55 - 0.5)(0.55 - 0.6)}{(0.4 - 0.5)(0.4 - 0.6)} \right]^2 = (-0.125)^2 = 0.015625$$

and similarly

$$[l_1(x)]^2 = (0.75)^2 = 0.5625,$$
$$[l_2(x)]^2 = (0.375)^2 = 0.140625.$$

Also

$$l'_0(x_0) = \frac{1}{0.4 - 0.5} + \frac{1}{0.4 - 0.6} = -15, \ x - x_0 = 0.55 - 0.4 = 0.15,$$

and similarly

$$l'_1(x_1) = 0, \qquad x - x_1 = 0.05,$$

$$l'_2(x_2) = 15, \qquad x - x_2 = -0.05.$$

Then

$$
\begin{aligned}
f(0.55) &= [1 - 2(-15)(0.15)](0.015625)(0.3894) \\
&\quad + [1 - 2(0)(0.05)](0.5625)(0.4794) \\
&\quad + [1 - 2(15)(-0.05)](0.140625)(0.5646) \\
&\quad + (0.15)(0.015625)(0.9211) + (0.05)(0.5625)(0.8776) \\
&\quad + (-0.05)(0.140625)(0.8253) + R_5(0.55) \\
&= 0.0334640 + 0.2696625 + 0.1984922 \\
&\quad + 0.0021588 + 0.0246825 - 0.0058029 + R_5(0.55) \\
&= 0.5226571 + R_5(0.55).
\end{aligned}
$$

The error function for this problem is

$$R_5(0.55) = \frac{f^{(6)}(\zeta)}{6!}[\pi(0.55)]^2 = \frac{f^{(6)}(\zeta)}{6!}[-0.375]^2 \times 10^{-6}.$$

If it is known that $f(x) = \sin x$, then

$$R_5(0.55) = 195.3125 \times 10^{-12} \sin \zeta.$$

Since $0.4 \le \zeta \le 0.6$, then $\sin 0.4 \le \sin \zeta \le \sin 0.6$. Hence

$$0.3894 \times 195.3125 \times 10^{-12} \le R_5(0.55) \le 195.3125 \times 10^{-12} \times 0.5646$$

or

$$8 \times 10^{-11} \le R_5(0.55) \le 12 \times 10^{-11}.$$

At first glance it would appear that the interpolation in a four-place table to obtain sin 0.55 produced a result accurate to about ten decimal places. As far as truncation error alone is concerned, this is true. However, the accumulation of error in the computation of $f(0.55)$ due to four-place data would permit only at most four places of accuracy in the result. The value of sin 0.55 in a four-place table is 0.5227, which is exactly the value obtained when the value computed above is rounded to four places.

Exercises

1. Write Equation 8.2.15 in terms of x, x_0, x_1 and $f(x)$ for $m = 2$.

2. If $m = 5$ and $f(x) = e^x$ while $x_0 = 1$, $x_1 = 3$, $x_2 = 5$, $x_3 = 6$, then $x_4 = 8$, evaluate $R_9(2)$.

3. In Example 8.2.2, it was concluded that, since $0.4 \le \zeta \le 0.6$, $\sin 0.4 \le \sin \zeta \le \sin 0.6$. If in general ζ lies in the range $a \le \zeta \le b$, is $\sin a \le \sin \zeta \le \sin b$?

8.3 Gaussian Quadrature

One approach in developing a quadrature formula is to approximate an integral by using an approximating polynomial to replace the integrand, i.e., to let

$$\int_a^b f(x)\,dx = \int_a^b P(x)\,dx + \int_a^b R(x)\,dx. \tag{8.3.1}$$

For the methods discussed in Chapter 4, the polynomial $P(x)$ was of degree $m - 1$. Use of the Hermite interpolation formula leads to a formula in which this polynomial is replaced by a polynomial, $P_{2m-1}(x)$, of degree $2m - 1$ or less.

To allow greater generality the integral to be evaluated in this section is $\int_a^b w(x) f(x)\,dx$, where $w(x)$ is a so-called weighting function. Therefore Equation 8.3.1 is to be replaced by

$$\int_a^b w(x) f(x)\,dx = \int_a^b w(x)\,P_{2m-1}(x)\,dx + \int_a^b w(x)\,R_{2m-1}(x)\,dx. \tag{8.3.2}$$

If now $P_{2m-1}(x)$ is the Hermite approximation for $f(x)$ of Equation 8.2.15, Equation 8.3.2 may be written as

$$\int_a^b w(x) f(x)\,dx = \sum_{k=0}^{m-1} f(x_k) \int_a^b w(x)\,h_k(x)\,dx$$
$$+ \sum_{k=0}^{m-1} f'(x_k) \int_a^b w(x)\,\bar{h}_k(x)\,dx + E_{2m-1}, \tag{8.3.3}$$

where $h_k(x)$ and $\bar{h}_k(x)$ are as defined in Equation 8.2.14 and $f'(x_k)$ denotes, as usual, the derivative of $f(x)$ at x_k. From Equation 8.2.16

$$E_{2m-1} = \frac{1}{(2m)!} \int_a^b w(x)\,[\pi(x)]^2 f^{(2m)}(\zeta)\,dx. \tag{8.3.4}$$

The second law of the mean for integrals states that, if $\alpha(x)$, $\beta(x)$ and $\alpha(x)\beta(x)$ are integrable functions in (a, b) and if $\alpha(x)$ does not change sign in (a, b), then

$$\int_a^b \alpha(x)\,\beta(x)\,dx = \beta(\eta) \int_a^b \alpha(x)\,dx \tag{8.3.5}$$

for some η in (a, b). Thus, if $w(x) \geq 0$ in (a, b), then Equation 8.3.4 may be rewritten in the form

$$E_{2m-1} = \frac{f^{(2m)}(\eta)}{(2m)!} \int_a^b w(x)\,[\pi(x)]^2\,dx. \tag{8.3.6}$$

For the integration formulas to follow, $w(x)$ will generally be chosen nonnegative in (a, b) so that the error term to apply will be E_{2m-1}, as displayed in Equation 8.3.6.

From Equation 8.3.6, it is apparent that if $f(x)$ is a polynomial of degree $2m - 1$ or less, $f^{(2m)}(\eta) = 0$ and $E_{2m-1} \equiv 0$, whereas for $f(x)$ a polynomial of degree $2m$ or greater, $E_{2m-1} \not\equiv 0$. A quadrature formula which possesses such a property is said to have a degree of precision equal to $2m - 1$. That is:

Definition 8.3.1 If a quadrature formula yields exact results for $f(x)$ an arbitrary polynomial of degree r or less but fails to give exact results for at least one polynomial of degree $r + 1$, it is said to possess *degree of precision* equal to r.

The Hermite quadrature formula of Equation 8.3.3 has degree of precision $2m - 1$. If now the abscissas $x_0, x_1, \ldots, x_{m-1}$ used in this formula are chosen in such a way that the coefficients associated with the derivative terms vanish, i.e., for $k = 0, 1, \ldots, m - 1$,

$$\int_a^b w(x) \, \bar{h}_k(x) \, dx = 0, \tag{8.3.7}$$

the resulting formula will still have degree of precision $2m - 1$ but will be obtained by fitting $f(x)$ only at m points.

Using the definition of $\bar{h}_k(x)$ of Equation 8.2.14, Equation 8.3.7 becomes, for $k = 0, 1, \ldots, m - 1$,

$$\int_a^b w(x) \, \bar{h}_k(x) \, dx = \int_a^b w(x) \, (x - x_k) \, [l_k(x)]^2 \, dx = 0 \tag{8.3.8}$$

or, replacing one of the factors, $l_k(x)$, by the form as given in Equation 8.1.5,

$$\int_a^b w(x) \, \bar{h}_k(x) \, dx = \int_a^b \frac{w(x)\pi(x)l_k(x) \, dx}{\pi'(x_k)} = 0, \tag{8.3.9}$$

where, as before,

$$\pi(x) = (x - x_0)(x - x_1) \ldots (x - x_{m-1}) \tag{8.3.10}$$

is a polynomial of degree m.

The condition of Equation 8.3.9 will certainly be met if $x_0, x_1, \ldots, x_{m-1}$ are chosen such that $\pi(x)$ is orthogonal to each $l_k(x)$ over the interval (a, b), with respect to the weighting function $w(x)$. Since the $l_k(x)$ $(k = 0, 1, \ldots, m - 1)$ are polynomials of degree $m - 1$, a sufficient condition that $\pi(x)$ be orthogonal to the polynomials $l_k(x)$ is that $\pi(x)$ be orthogonal to *all* polynomials of degree $m - 1$ or less. It can be shown in fact that

$$\int_a^b w(x) f(x)\, dx = \sum_{k=0}^{m-1} f(x_k) \int_a^b w(x)\, h_k(x)\, dx + E_{2m-1} \qquad (8.3.11)$$

if and only if $\pi(x)$ is orthogonal to every polynomial $P(x)$ of degree less than m, with respect to $w(x)$, over (a, b).

Reference to the definitions of $h_k(x)$ and $\bar{h}_k(x)$ of Equation 8.2.14 shows that $h_k(x) = [l_k(x)]^2 - 2l'_k(x_k)\, \bar{h}_k(x)$. With this definition and Equation 8.3.7, Equation 8.3.11 can be written as

$$\int_a^b w(x) f(x)\, dx = \sum_{k=0}^{m-1} f(x_k) \int_a^b w(x)\, [l_k(x)]^2\, dx + E_{2m-1}. \qquad (8.3.12)$$

Quadrature formulas of the form of Equation 8.3.11 or Equation 8.3.12 are usually called Gaussian quadrature formulas.

Since the condition which must be satisfied for Equation 8.3.11 to be valid is that $\pi(x)$ must be orthogonal to all polynomials of less than a specified degree and since least-squares polynomials are derived to satisfy just such conditions, least-squares polynomials are used in Equation 8.3.11 to give rise to various quadrature formulas of the Gaussian type.

In the following sections certain least-squares Gaussian quadrature formulas are given and their use illustrated but without details of the theoretical developments.

Exercises

1. If $w(x)$ is not necessarily nonnegative in (a, b), but $f(x)$ is any polynomial of degree $2m - 1$ or less, does $E_{2m-1} = 0$? Does the degree of precision of the quadrature formula for $\int_a^b w(x) f(x)\, dx$ depend upon $w(x)$?

2. Derive Equation 8.3.12 from Equation 8.3.11, making use of Equations 8.3.7 and 8.2.14.

8.4 Gauss-Legendre Quadrature

It is shown in the preceding section that, for specified a, b and $w(x)$, quadrature formulas can be obtained which have degree of precision $2m - 1$ but which require only m points for evaluation provided only that the condition for orthogonality is satisfied.

The Legendre least-squares polynomial of degree m is defined as orthogonal to all polynomials of degree less than m with respect to a weight function of unity over the interval $(-1, 1)$. If the abscissas $x_0, x_1, \ldots, x_{m-1}$ of Equation 8.3.10 are chosen to be the zeros of the mth

Legendre polynomial $L_m(x)$, then

$$\pi(x) = \frac{1}{A_m} L_m(x), \tag{8.4.1}$$

where

$$A_m = \frac{(2m)!}{2^m m!}. \tag{8.4.2}$$

Then the quadrature formula of Equation 8.3.11 can be shown to become

$$\int_{-1}^{1} f(x)\, dx = \sum_{k=0}^{m-1} H_k f(x_k) + E_{2m-1}, \tag{8.4.3}$$

where

$$H_k = \frac{2(1 - x_k^2)}{(m+1)^2 [L_{m+1}(x_k)]^2} = \frac{2}{(1 - x_k^2)[L'_m(x_k)]^2}, \tag{8.4.4}$$

$$E_{2m-1} = \frac{2^{2m+1}(m!)^4}{(2m+1)(2m!)^3} f^{(2m)}(\eta), \tag{8.4.5}$$

and the x_k are the roots of $L_m(x) = 0$, and η is between -1 and 1. Equation 8.4.3 is the Gauss-Legendre quadrature formula.

EXAMPLE 8.4.1   Exhibit the Gauss-Legendre quadrature formula for $m = 3$.

Solution: The Legendre polynomial $L_3(x)$ is

$$L_3(x) = \tfrac{1}{2}(5x^3 - 3x)$$

with zeros

$$x = 0 \quad \text{and} \quad x = \pm\sqrt{\tfrac{3}{5}}.$$

Then, if $x_0 = -\sqrt{\tfrac{3}{5}}$, $x_1 = 0$, $x_2 = \sqrt{\tfrac{3}{5}}$, since $L_4(x) = \tfrac{1}{8}(35x^4 - 30x^2 + 3)$ (or $L'_3(x) = \tfrac{1}{2}(15x^2 - 3)$),

$$H_0 = H_2 = 2\left(1 - \frac{3}{5}\right) \bigg/ 4^2\left[\frac{35(\tfrac{3}{5})^2 - 30(\tfrac{3}{5}) + 3}{8}\right]^2 = +\frac{5}{9},$$

and similarly

$$H_1 = \frac{2}{4^2(\tfrac{3}{8})^2} = \frac{8}{9}.$$

The error term for $m = 3$ is

$$E_5 = \frac{2^7(3!)^4}{7(6!)^3} f^{(6)}(\eta) = \frac{1}{15750} f^{(6)}(\eta).$$

Therefore the complete quadrature formula is

$$\int_{-1}^{1} f(x)\, dx = \tfrac{1}{9}[5 f(-\sqrt{\tfrac{3}{5}}) + 8 f(0) + 5 f(\sqrt{\tfrac{3}{5}})] + \frac{f^{(6)}(\eta)}{15750}.$$

A characteristic of all Gauss-Legendre quadrature formulas is illustrated in Example 8.4.1. Because all Legendre polynomials contain either all even powers or all odd powers, the zeros of all $L_m(x)$ are symmetric about the origin, for example, x_0 and x_2 as shown in Example 8.4.1. Hence, the terms $L_{m+1}(x_i)$ or $L'_m(x_i)$ are the same for the two values of each symmetric pair of values and the H_i for these two zeros are equal.

The $L_m(x)$, x_i and H_i for $2 \le m \le 5$ are given in Table 8.4.1.

TABLE 8.4.1

m	$L_m(x)$	x_i	H_i
2	$\frac{1}{2}(3x^2 - 1)$	± 0.57735	1
3	$\frac{1}{2}(5x^3 - 3x)$	$\begin{cases} 0 \\ \pm 0.774597 \end{cases}$	$\begin{cases} \frac{8}{9} \\ \frac{5}{9} \end{cases}$
4	$\frac{1}{8}(35x^4 - 30x^2 + 3)$	$\begin{cases} \pm 0.339981 \\ \pm 0.861136 \end{cases}$	$\begin{cases} 0.652145 \\ 0.347855 \end{cases}$
5	$\frac{1}{8}(63x^5 - 70x^3 + 15x)$	$\begin{cases} 0 \\ \pm 0.538469 \\ \pm 0.906180 \end{cases}$	$\begin{cases} 0.568889 \\ 0.478629 \\ 0.236927 \end{cases}$

NOTE: The x_i are such that $L_m(x_i) = 0$.

While the Gauss-Legendre quadrature formula involves the interval $(-1, 1)$, any finite interval can be transformed into this interval by a linear transformation of variable. As an illustration of this, consider the following example.

EXAMPLE 8.4.2   Use the quadrature formula found in Example 8.4.1 to evaluate the integral

$$I = \int_0^{\pi/2} \frac{dx}{4 \cos^2 x + 9 \sin^2 x}.$$

Solution: The interval $\left(0, \frac{\pi}{2}\right)$ is first transformed to $(-1, 1)$ by the transformation of variable: $y = \frac{4}{\pi} x - 1$, $dy = \frac{4}{\pi} dx$. Hence

$$I = \frac{\pi}{4} \int_{-1}^1 \frac{dy}{4 \cos^2 \frac{\pi}{4}(y + 1) + 9 \sin^2 \frac{\pi}{4}(y + 1)}.$$

The quadrature formula developed in Example 8.4.1 (or row 2, Table 8.4.1) requires $f(-0.7746)$, $f(0.7746)$ and $f(0)$ (rounding to four decimal places).

$$f(-0.7746) = 0.24066,$$
$$f(0.7746) = 0.11306,$$
$$f(0) = 0.15384.$$

Then

$$I = \frac{1}{9} \cdot \frac{\pi}{4}(5 \times 0.24066 + 8 \times 0.15384 + 5 \times 0.11306) = 0.2617.$$

As a check on the accuracy, a table of definite integrals gives the value of this integral as $\frac{\pi}{12} \approx 0.2618$.

Equation 8.4.3 leads to other quadrature formulas by changing the interval of integration. If in particular it is desired to obtain a formula for

$$I = \int_0^1 f(y)\, dy, \tag{8.4.6}$$

let $y = \frac{x+1}{2}$; then $y = 0$ when $x = -1$; $y = 1$ when $x = 1$; $dx = 2dy$. Then the integral is transformed into

$$I = \frac{1}{2}\int_{-1}^1 f\left(\frac{x+1}{2}\right) dx, \tag{8.4.7}$$

and Equation 8.4.3 becomes

$$\int_0^1 f(y)\, dy = \frac{1}{2}\int_{-1}^1 f\left(\frac{x+1}{2}\right) dx = \sum_{k=0}^{m-1} W_k f(y_k) + E_{2m-1}, \tag{8.4.8}$$

where

$$y_k = \frac{x_k + 1}{2}, \qquad W_k = \tfrac{1}{2} H_k,$$

and x_k and H_k are as defined for Equation 8.4.3.

The tabulation for Equation 8.4.8, corresponding to Table 8.4.1 is given in Table 8.4.2.

It is of interest to note that the symmetry of x_k is lost on the y_k but that of H_k is retained in W_k.

EXAMPLE 8.4.3   Use Table 8.4.2 with $m = 3$ to evaluate the integral

$$I = \int_0^1 \frac{1+x^2}{1+x^4}\, dx.$$

TABLE 8.4.2

m	$L_m(x)$	y_k	W_k
2	$\frac{1}{2}(3x^2 - 1)$	$\begin{cases} 0.21132 \\ 0.78867 \end{cases}$	$\begin{cases} \frac{1}{2} \\ \frac{1}{2} \end{cases}$
3	$\frac{1}{2}(5x^3 - 3x)$	$\begin{cases} 0.11270 \\ 0.50000 \\ 0.88730 \end{cases}$	$\begin{cases} 0.27778 \\ 0.44444 \\ 0.27778 \end{cases}$
4	$\frac{1}{8}(35x^4 - 30x^2 + 3)$	$\begin{cases} 0.06943 \\ 0.33000 \\ 0.66999 \\ 0.93057 \end{cases}$	$\begin{cases} 0.17393 \\ 0.32607 \\ 0.32607 \\ 0.17393 \end{cases}$
5	$\frac{1}{8}(63x^5 - 70x^3 + 15x)$	$\begin{cases} 0.04691 \\ 0.23077 \\ 0.50000 \\ 0.76923 \\ 0.95309 \end{cases}$	$\begin{cases} 0.11846 \\ 0.23931 \\ 0.28444 \\ 0.23931 \\ 0.11846 \end{cases}$

Solution: The quadrature formula for this case is (rounding to four decimal places)

$$I = \frac{1}{18} \{5f(0.1127) + 8f(0.5) + 5f(0.8873)\}$$

$$= \frac{1}{18} \left\{ 5 \frac{1 + \overline{0.1127}^2}{1 + \overline{0.1127}^4} + 8 \frac{1 + \overline{0.5}^2}{1 + \overline{0.5}^4} + 5 \frac{1 + \overline{0.8873}^2}{1 + \overline{0.8873}^4} \right\}$$

$$= \frac{1}{18} \{5(1.01253) + 8(1.17647) + 5(1.10340)\} = \frac{19.99141}{18} = 1.11062.$$

A table of definite integrals gives the value of this integral as

$$\frac{\pi}{4} \sqrt{2} \approx 1.11055.$$

EXAMPLE 8.4.4   Use the Gauss-Legendre quadrature formula for $m = 3$ to obtain the formula for $\tan^{-1} x$ by integrating

$$\tan^{-1} x = \int_0^x \frac{dt}{1 + t^2}.$$

Use the formula to find $\tan^{-1} 1$.

Solution: By the transformation

$$u = \frac{t}{x} \quad \text{or} \quad t = xu; \quad t = 0, \quad u = 0;$$

$$t = x, \quad u = 1; \quad dt = x \, du,$$

the integral is transformed into

$$\tan^{-1} x = x \int_0^1 \frac{du}{1 + x^2 u^2}.$$

Using the quadrature formula of Equation 8.4.8 for $m = 3$,

$$\tan^{-1} x = \frac{x}{18}\left\{\frac{5}{1 + (0.11270x)^2} + \frac{8}{1 + (0.5x)^2} + \frac{5}{1 + (0.8873x)^2}\right\}$$

$$= \frac{x}{18}\left\{\frac{5}{1 + 0.0127x^2} + \frac{8}{1.25x^2} + \frac{5}{1 + 0.7873x^2}\right\}.$$

Then

$$\tan^{-1} 1 = \frac{1}{18}\left\{\frac{5}{1.0127} + \frac{8}{1.25} + \frac{5}{1.7873}\right\} = 0.7853.$$

The exact answer is $\pi/4 \approx 0.7854$.

EXAMPLE 8.4.5   Compare the results of the Gauss-Legendre quadrature formula evaluation of

$$I = \int_0^1 \frac{\log x \, dx}{1 - x}$$

for $m = 3, 4$ and 5.

Solution: It is known that $I = \dfrac{-\pi^2}{6} \approx -1.6449$. Using Equation 8.4.8 and 8.4.5, together with Table 8.4.2, with $f(x) = \dfrac{\log x}{1 - x}$, the approximations to I are

m	I	E_{2m-1}
3	−1.594	$\dfrac{f^{(6)}(\eta)}{15750}$
4	−1.614	$\dfrac{f^{(8)}(\eta)}{3,472,875}$
5	−1.624	$\dfrac{f^{(10)}(\eta)}{1,237,732,650}$

Thus, the approximations appear to be approaching the correct value of I slowly. Since the denominator of the error-term E_{2m-1} is huge, this must imply that the even derivatives of $f(x)$ can become large. It can be shown that

$$f^{(2m)}(x) = (2m)! \frac{x \log x + x - 1}{x(1 - x)^{2m+1}} - \sum_{r=2}^{2m} \frac{(2m)!}{rx^r(1 - x)^{2m-r+1}},$$

and it is seen that this quantity can become large in $(0, 1)$.

Exercises

1. $\pi(x)$ is defined as

$$\pi(x) = (x - x_0)(x - x_1) \cdots (x - x_{m-1}).$$

Show that $\dfrac{1}{A_m} L_m(x) = \pi(x)$ for a certain selection of x_0, x_1 and x_2 when $m = 3$.

2. Estimate the error term E_5 for the quadrature of Examples 8.4.2 and 8.4.3.

3. If $\int_a^b w(x) f(x) \, dx = \sum_{k=0}^{n-1} W_k f(x_k) + E_{2n-1}$, show that $\int_o^b w(x) \, dx = \sum_{k=0}^{n-1} W_k$.

Verify this for the W_k listed in Table 8.4.2.

8.5   Gauss-Laguerre Quadrature

Laguerre least-squares polynomials are defined with respect to a weight function of

$$w(x) = e^{-x} \tag{8.5.1}$$

over the semi-infinite interval $(0, \infty)$. Hence if the integral to be evaluated is expressed in the form

$$I = \int_0^\infty e^{-x} f(x) \, dx, \tag{8.5.2}$$

the Laguerre polynomials may be used in a quadrature formula for evaluation of this integral. In this case

$$\pi(x) = (-1)^m \mathcal{L}_m(x), \tag{8.5.3}$$

where $\mathcal{L}_m(x)$ is the Laguerre least-squares polynomial of degree m. The quadrature formula of Equation 8.3.11 can be written in the form

$$I = \int_0^\infty e^{-x} f(x) \, dx = \sum_{k=0}^{m-1} H_k f(x_k) + E_{2m-1}, \tag{8.5.4}$$

where the x_k are the zeros of $\mathcal{L}_m(x)$ and where

$$H_i = \frac{(m!)^2}{x_i[\mathcal{L}'_m(x_i)]^2} = \frac{(m!)^2 x_i}{[\mathcal{L}_{m+1}(x_i)]^2} \tag{8.5.5}$$

and

$$E_{2m-1} = \frac{(m!)^2}{(2m)!} f^{(2m)}(\eta). \tag{8.5.6}$$

EXAMPLE 8.5.1 Develop the Gauss-Laguerre quadrature formula for $m = 2$.

Solution: The second-degree Laguerre polynomial is

$$\mathcal{L}_2(x) = 2 - 4x + x^2$$

with zeros of $2 \pm \sqrt{2}$.

Then

$$\mathcal{L}'_2(x_i) = -4 + 2x_i = \pm 2\sqrt{2},$$

$$[\mathcal{L}'_2(x_i)]^2 = 8,$$

and

$$H_0 = \frac{4}{8(2 - \sqrt{2})} = \frac{2 + \sqrt{2}}{4}, \qquad H_1 = \frac{4}{8(2 + \sqrt{2})} = \frac{2 - \sqrt{2}}{4}.$$

The error term is

$$E_{2m-1} = \frac{(2!)^2}{4!} f^{(4)}(\eta) = \frac{f^{(4)}(\eta)}{6}.$$

The complete quadrature formula is, then,

$$I = \int_0^\infty e^{-x} f(x)\,dx = \frac{1}{4}[(2 + \sqrt{2})f(2 - \sqrt{2})$$

$$+ (2 - \sqrt{2})f(2 + \sqrt{2})] + \frac{f^{(4)}(\eta)}{6}.$$

As for the Gauss-Legendre quadrature, a tabulation of the Laguerre polynomials, the zeros (x_k), and the values of H_i is convenient and such a tabulation is given in Table 8.5.1 for $2 \leq m \leq 5$.

EXAMPLE 8.5.2 Use the Gauss-Laguerre quadrature formula for $m = 3$ to evaluate the integral

$$I = \int_0^\infty \frac{e^{-x}\,dx}{x + 4}.$$

Solution: Referring to Table 8.5.1, the formula for $m = 3$ and $f(x) = \dfrac{1}{x + 4}$ is given by

$$\int_0^\infty \frac{e^{-x}\,dx}{x + 4} \approx \frac{0.711093}{4.415775} + \frac{0.278518}{6.29428} + \frac{0.0103893}{10.289945}$$

$$\approx 0.16103 + 0.04425 + 0.00101 = 0.20629.$$

The error term is $E_5 = \dfrac{(3!)^2}{6!} f^{(6)}(\eta)$. Since $f^{(6)}(x) = \dfrac{6!}{(x + 4)^7}$, then $f^6(x) \leq \dfrac{6!}{4^7}$ in $(0, \infty)$. Hence, $E_5 \leq \dfrac{(3!)^2\,6!}{6!\,4^7} < 0.0022.$

TABLE 8.5.1

m	$\mathscr{L}_m(x)$	x_i	H_i
2	$2 - 4x + x^2$	0.585786	0.853553
		3.414214	0.146447
3	$6 - 18x + 9x^2 - x^3$	0.415775	0.711093
		2.294280	0.278518
		6.289945	0.0103893
4	$24 - 96x + 72x^2 - 16x^3$ $+ x^4$	0.322548	0.603154
		1.745761	0.357419
		4.536620	0.0388879
		9.395071	0.000539295
5	$120 - 600x + 600x^2 - 200x^3$ $+ 25x^4 - x^5$	0.263560	0.521756
		1.413403	0.398667
		3.596426	0.0759424
		7.085810	0.00361176
		12.640801	0.00002337

Exercises

1. Can the integral $I_1 = \displaystyle\int_0^\infty e^{-x} f(x)\, dx$ be converted to the integral $I_2 = \displaystyle\int_0^1 g(u)\, du$ by means of the transformation $x = \dfrac{u}{1 - u}$? If so, compare the Gauss-Laguerre approximation for I_1 with the Gauss-Legendre approximation for I_2 for $m = 2$.

2. Use the Gauss-Laguerre quadrature formula to approximate

$$I = \int_0^\infty x e^{-x} \sin x \, dx$$

for $m = 3, 4, 5$. Discuss the error in view of the fact that $I = \frac{1}{2}$.

8.6　Gauss-Chebychev Quadrature

A Chebychev least-squares polynomial, $T_m(x)$, is defined for a weight function of

$$w(x) = \frac{1}{\sqrt{1 - x^2}} \tag{8.6.1}$$

over the interval $(-1, 1)$. In this case

$$\pi(x) = \frac{1}{2^{m-1}} T_m(x). \tag{8.6.2}$$

The Chebychev quadrature formula is

$$\int_{-1}^{1} \frac{f(x)}{\sqrt{1-x^2}}\,dx = \sum_{k=0}^{m-1} H_k f(x_k) + E_{2m-1}, \qquad (8.6.3)$$

where the x_k are the zeros of the mth Chebychev polynomial, $T_m(x)$,

$$H_k = -\frac{\pi}{T'_m(x_i)\,T_{m+1}(x_i)}, \qquad (8.6.4)$$

and

$$E_{2m-1} = \frac{2\pi}{2^{2m}(2m)!} f^{(2m)}(\eta) \qquad |\eta| < 1. \qquad (8.6.5)$$

Here π is the irrational number π and is not related to $\pi(x)$.
Since

$$T_m(x) = \cos(m\cos^{-1} x), \qquad (8.6.6)$$

it can be shown that the zeros of $T_m(x)$ are

$$x_i = \cos\left[\frac{(2i+1)\pi}{2m}\right], \qquad i = 0, 1, \ldots, m-1. \qquad (8.6.7)$$

In addition

$$T'_m(x_i) = \frac{(-1)^i m}{\sin \alpha}, \qquad T_{m+1}(x_i) = (-1)^{i+1}\sin \alpha_i, \qquad (8.6.8)$$

where

$$\alpha_i = \frac{2i+1}{2m}\pi, \qquad i = 0, 1, \ldots, m-1. \qquad (8.6.9)$$

Hence Equation 8.6.4 reduces to the very simple form

$$H_k = \frac{\pi}{m}, \qquad (8.6.10)$$

and all weights in Equation 8.6.3 are equal. Equation 8.6.3 can, therefore, be written as

$$\int_{-1}^{1} \frac{f(x)}{\sqrt{1-x^2}}\,dx = \frac{\pi}{m}\sum_{k=0}^{m-1} f\left(\cos\frac{2k+1}{2m}\pi\right)$$

$$+ \frac{2\pi}{2^{2m}(2m)!} f^{(2m)}(\eta) \quad (8.6.11)$$

EXAMPLE 8.6.1 Use the Gauss-Chebychev quadrature formula for $m = 3$ to evaluate the integral

$$I = \int_{-1}^{1} \frac{\cos x}{\sqrt{1-x^2}}\,dx.$$

Solution: Using Equation 8.6.11 for this integral gives

$$I = \frac{\pi}{3}\left[\cos\left(\cos\frac{\pi}{6}\right) + \cos\left(\cos\frac{3\pi}{6}\right) + \cos\left(\cos\frac{5\pi}{6}\right)\right] + \frac{\pi}{23040}f^6(\eta)$$

$$\approx \frac{\pi}{3}\left[\cos 0.866 + \cos 0 + \cos 0.866\right] + \frac{\pi}{23040}f^6(\eta)$$

$$= 2.40395 + \frac{\pi}{23040}f^{(6)}(\eta).$$

Since $f(x) = \cos x$,

$$\left|\frac{\pi f^6(\eta)}{23040}\right| < \frac{\pi}{23040} = 0.000136.$$

Exercise

If the integral $I = \int_{-1}^{1} \frac{f(x)}{\sqrt{1-x^2}}\,dx$ is to be approximated, discuss the relative merits of the Gauss-Legendre and the Gauss-Chebychev formulas. Carry out some of the evaluation in each case for $m = 3$.

8.7   Gauss-Hermite Quadrature

One final least-squares polynomial and its resulting quadrature formula are considered here. In the case of a weighting function

$$w(x) = e^{-x^2} \tag{8.7.1}$$

over the infinite interval $(-\infty, \infty)$, the Hermite polynomial is used:

$$\pi(x) = \frac{1}{2^m} H_m(x), \tag{8.7.2}$$

where $H_m(x)$ is the mth Hermite polynomial. The resulting quadrature formula in its simplest form is

$$\int_{-\infty}^{\infty} e^{-x^2} f(x)\,dx = \sum_{k=0}^{m-1} H_k f(x_k) + E_{2m-1}, \tag{8.7.3}$$

where the x_k are the zeros of the mth Hermite polynomial,

$$H_k = \frac{2^{m+1}m!\sqrt{\pi}}{[H'_m(x_k)]^2} = \frac{2^{m+1}m!\sqrt{\pi}}{[H_{m+1}(x_k)]^2} \tag{8.7.4}$$

and

$$E_{2m-1} = \frac{m!\sqrt{\pi}}{2^m(2m)!}f^{(2m)}(\eta). \tag{8.7.5}$$

The weight functions, H_k, and the abscissa values, x_k, are shown in Table 8.7.1, along with $H_m(x)$ for $2 \le m \le 5$.

TABLE 8.7.1

m	$H(x)$	x_k	H_k
2	$4x^2 - 2$	± 0.707107	0.886227
3	$8x^3 - 12x$	0	1.181636
		± 1.224745	0.295409
4	$16x^4 - 48x^2 + 12$	± 0.524648	0.804914
		± 1.650680	0.0813128
5	$32x^5 - 160x^3 + 120x$	0	0.945309
		± 0.958572	0.393619
		± 2.020183	0.0199532

NOTE: The x_k and H_k have the same symmetry characteristics as those for the Gauss-Legendre quadrature.

EXAMPLE 8.7.1　Verify the entries in Table 8.7.1, columns 3 and 4, for $m = 3$. What is the error term?

Solution:　Since

$$H_3(x) = 8x^3 - 12x = 4x(2x^2 - 3),$$

the zeros of $H_3(x)$ are $x = 0$ and $x = \pm \sqrt{\frac{3}{2}} = \pm \sqrt{6}/2 = \pm 1.224745$.
Using these values in Equation 8.7.4, since

$$H'_3(x) = 24x^2 - 12 = 12(2x^2 - 1),$$
$$H'_3(0) = -12,$$
$$H'_3 \left(\pm \sqrt{\frac{3}{2}} \right) = 12(3 - 1) = 24,$$

then

$$H_1 = \frac{2^4 3! \sqrt{\pi}}{(12)^2} = \frac{2}{3} \sqrt{\pi} = \frac{2}{3} \times 1.77245385 = 1.1816359$$

$$H_0 = H_2 = \frac{2^4 3! \sqrt{\pi}}{(24)^2} = \frac{\sqrt{\pi}}{6} = 0.29540898.$$

The error term for $m = 3$ is

$$E_{2m-1} = f^{(6)}(\eta) \frac{3! \sqrt{\pi}}{2^3 (6)!} = f^{(6)}(\eta) \frac{\sqrt{\pi}}{960} = 0.001846 f^{(6)}(\eta).$$

EXAMPLE 8.7.2　Use the Gauss-Hermite quadrature formula for $m = 3$ to evaluate the integral

$$I = \int_{-\infty}^{\infty} e^{-x} \cos x \, dx.$$

Solution: From Table 8.7.1, $x_0 = -1.224745$, $x_1 = 0$, $x_2 = 1.224745$, $H_1 = 1.181636$, $H_0 = H_2 = 0.295409$. Hence

$$I \approx 0.295409 \cos(-1.224745) + 1.181636 \cos 0$$
$$+ 0.295409 \cos(1.224745)$$
$$= 2 \times 0.295409 \cos(1.224745) + 1.181636$$
$$\approx 0.590818 \times 0.33923 + 1.181636$$
$$= 1.382059.$$

An upper bound on the error term is given by

$$|E_{2m-1}| = \left| \frac{3!\sqrt{\pi}f^{(2m)}(\zeta)}{2^3 6!} \right| < \left| \frac{\sqrt{\pi}}{960} \right| < 0.002.$$

Problems

8.1   By means of the Lagrange interpolation polynomial, determine the polynomial $P(x)$ of degree 5 or less which has the following values.

x	$P(x)$
1	3
2	4
4	7
8	6
9	3
10	1

8.2   Determine the Lagrange interpolation polynomial approximation to $\sin x$, using 5-place values of $\sin x$ at $0, \frac{\pi}{4}, \frac{\pi}{2}, \frac{3\pi}{4}$.

8.3   Find a good upper bound to the error in evaluating $\sin 0.7$, using the polynomial of Problem 8.2.

8.4   What is the maximum contribution of the rounding error in the approximation to $\sin 0.7$ in Problem 8.3?

8.5   Use the Hermite interpolation formula to find the polynomial $P_5(x)$ of degree 5 or less which approximates $\sqrt{x}$, using $x_k = 1, 8, 11$. Determine the error in using $P_5(5)$ as an approximation to $\sqrt{5}$.

8.6   Derive the error term displayed in Equation 8.2.16.

8.7   Verify the entries in Table 8.4.1 for $m = 4$.

8.8   Derive the error term for the Gauss-Legendre quadrature formula when $m = 4$.

8.9   Make use of the Gauss-Legendre formula and the fact that

$$\cos^{-1}\left(\frac{a-x}{a}\right) = \int_0^x \frac{du}{\sqrt{2au-u^2}}$$

to derive an approximation for $\cos^{-1}\left(\dfrac{a-x}{a}\right)$. Use this approximation to determine $\cos^{-1}\left(\frac{1}{2}\right)$. Determine the error in the approximation.

8.10   Find approximate values of

$$\int_0^\infty \sqrt{x}e^{-x}\,dx,$$

using $m = 3, 4, 5$. The value of this integral is $\sqrt{\pi}/2$. Determine the error in the approximations.

8.11   Derive the Gauss-Laguerre formula for the integral $\displaystyle\int_0^\infty e^{-ax}f(x)\,dx$.

8.12   Use $m = 3$ and the Gauss-Leguerre formula to find an approximation formula for

$$\Gamma(n+1) = a^{n+1}\int_0^\infty x^n e^{-ax}\,dx.$$

Approximate $\Gamma(3)$ and discuss its error.

8.13   If $f(x)$ is an even function, that is, $f(x) = f(-x)$, then

$$\int_{-\infty}^\infty e^{-ax^2}f(x)\,dx = 2\int_0^\infty e^{-ax^2}f(x)\,dx.$$

For an even function $f(x)$, compare the Gauss-Laguerre and the Gauss-Hermite formulas for $m = 3$.

8.14   Approximate

$$\int_4^7 \sqrt{1-x^2}\,dx$$

by the Gauss-Chebychev formula with $m = 4$. Determine the error.

Appendix A

Some Definitions of Concepts from Calculus

Definition A.1 The open interval (a, b) on the x-axis is the set of all points, x, such that $a < x < b$. The closed interval (a, b) on the x-axis is the set of all points, x, such that $a \leq x \leq b$.

Definition A.2 The limit of a function, $f(x)$, as x approaches a number a, real or complex, is the number b,

$$\lim_{x \to a} f(x) = b, \qquad (A.1)$$

if for every positive number ϵ there is a positive number δ such that $|f(x) - b| < \epsilon$ if only $|x - a| < \delta$.

Definition A.2 can be interpreted as follows: the $\lim_{x \to a} f(x)$ is b if whenever any positive number ϵ, no matter how small, is chosen, the distance from $f(x)$ to b can be made smaller than ϵ just by making x sufficiently close to a. Thus one may interpret $|f(x) - b|$ as being the *distance* from $f(x)$ to b at some value of x. The particular value of x to be used is any for which $|x - a| < \delta$. Hence, if $\lim_{x \to a} f(x) = b$, then there is some interval, perhaps very small, which contains a, such that, for every x in that interval, $f(x)$ differs from b by as little as one cares to make it.

Definition A.3 A function, $f(x)$, is continuous at $x = a$ if $\lim_{x \to a} f(x) = f(a)$.

EXAMPLE A.1 Let $f(x) = \dfrac{1}{x - 1}$. Is $f(x)$ continuous at $x = 1$?

Solution: A glance at the graph of $f(x)$ in Figure A.1 is sufficient to convince one that $f(x)$ is not continuous at $x = 1$. This "hunch" should

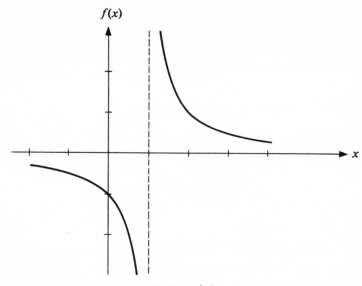

FIGURE A.1

now be rigorously verified, at least with the degree of rigor now available. Thus to show that $f(x)$ is not continuous at $x = 1$, it is sufficient to show that $\lim\limits_{x \to 1} f(x)$ is not $f(1)$. In this case $f(1) = \dfrac{1}{1 - 1} = \dfrac{1}{0}$, which is not defined. Further, the $\lim\limits_{x \to 1} \dfrac{1}{x - 1}$ is not defined, so that it is impossible to have $\lim\limits_{x \to 0} \dfrac{1}{x - 1} = f(1)$.

EXAMPLE A.2   The step function $f(x)$ defined by

$$f(x) = \begin{cases} x & \text{for} \quad x < 2, \\ x - 2 & \text{for} \quad x \geq 2, \end{cases}$$

is not continuous at $x = 2$. This may be seen since $f(2) = 0$ by definition, whereas no matter how small an interval about $x = 2$ is chosen there are always values of x in that interval for which $x < 2$. Hence, there are always values of x in any interval containing 2 for which $f(x)$ is nearly 2 and not 0.

One fact which is often used in this book is that if $f(x)$ is continuous for all x in a closed interval (a, b), then $f(x)$ is bounded over that interval. That is, there is a constant, M, such that $|f(x)| \leq M$ for all x in (a, b).

Appendix B

Some Theorems on the Derivative

One of the most commonly used concepts in almost any mathematical development is that of the derivative. Since this is true, a working definition and some of the more useful properties of the derivative are needed.

Definition B.1   The derivative of the function $f(x)$ at $x = a$ is defined as

$$\frac{df(x)}{dx}\bigg|_{x=a} = \lim_{h \to 0} \frac{f(a + h) - f(a)}{h} \tag{B.1}$$

if the limit on the right side of this equation exists.

If a function $f(x)$ is differentiable at $x = a$, then, of course, $f(x)$ is continuous at $x = a$. Some properties closely related to continuity and differentiability are as follows:

THEOREM B.1   (*Theorem of the Mean*)   If $f(x)$ is differentiable on the closed interval (a, b), then there exists a value $x = \delta$ where δ is between a and b, such that

$$\frac{f(b) - f(a)}{b - a} = f'(\delta). \tag{B.2}$$

The Theorem of the Mean receives application in the truncation-error analysis associated with curve fitting. A theorem which contains the Theorem of the Mean as a special case is the following:

THEOREM B.2   (*Taylor's Theorem*)   If $f(x)$ and its first n derivatives are single-valued and continuous in the closed interval (a, b), then

$$f(b) = f(a) + f'(a)(b - a) + \cdots + \frac{f^{(n-1)}(a)(b - a)^{n-1}}{(n - 1)!} + R_n(b), \tag{B.3}$$

169

where $R_n(b)$ can be given as

$$R_n(b) = \frac{f^{(n)}(\delta)(b - a)^n}{n!} \; ; \tag{B.4}$$

here δ is some value of x between a and b.

Thus, if $n = 1$, Equations B.3 and B.4 become

$$f(b) = f(a) + R_1(b), \tag{B.5}$$

$$R_1(b) = f'(\delta)(b - a). \tag{B.6}$$

Substituting Equation B.6 into Equation B.5 and rearranging the result produces

$$\frac{f(b) - f(a)}{b - a} = f'(\delta), \tag{B.7}$$

which is precisely Equation B.2. Hence, the Theorem of the Mean is a special case of Taylor's Theorem.

In the discussion of the numerical solution of ordinary differential equations with a one-point initial condition by the Runge-Kutta method, use is made of a more general version of the expansion given in Equation B.3. The more general version requires the Taylor's series expansion of a function of two variables.

THEOREM B.3 (*Taylor's Theorem for a Function of Two Variables*) If $f(x, y)$ and all of its first n partial derivatives are single-valued and continuous in the closed rectangle $a \le x \le c, b \le y \le d$, then

$$f(x + h, y + k) = f(x, y) + \frac{\partial f}{\partial x} h + \frac{\partial f}{\partial y} k$$

$$+ \frac{1}{2!}\left[\frac{\partial^2 f}{\partial x^2} h^2 + 2 \frac{\partial^2 f}{\partial x \partial y} hk + \frac{\partial^2 f}{\partial y^2} k^2\right]$$

$$+ \cdots + \frac{1}{(n-1)!} \sum_{i=0}^{n-1} \frac{(n-1)!}{(n-i-1)!\, i!} \frac{\partial^{n-1} f}{\partial x^{n-1-i} \partial y^i} h^{n-1-i} k^i$$

$$+ \frac{1}{n!} \sum_{i=0}^{n} \frac{n!}{(n-i)!\, i!} \frac{\partial^n f(\alpha, \beta)}{\partial x^{n-i} \partial y^i} h^{n-i} k^i, \tag{B.8}$$

where the partial derivatives of f are evaluated at (x, y), while α is some number between x and $x + h$, and β is some number between y and $y + k$.

Appendix C

Minima, Absolute and Relative

In the development of the least-squares curve-fitting procedures, and again in the method of solving a system of nonlinear algebraic equations, use must be made of minimizing a function of several variables. A careful distinction should be maintained between a relative minimum for a function, the absolute minimum of a function, and the minimum of a function over some closed region.

Definition C.1 A relative minimum of a function $f(x_1, x_2, \ldots, x_n)$ is a value $f(a_1, a_2, \ldots, a_n)$ such that for some region R which contains $(a_1, a_2, \ldots, a_n)$,

$$f(x_1, x_2, \ldots, x_n) \geq f(a_1, a_2, \ldots, a_n)$$

for all $(x_1, x_2, \ldots, x_n)$ in R.

An absolute minimum of a function $f(x_1, x_2, \ldots, x_n)$ is a value $f(a_1, a_2, \ldots, a_n)$, if it exists, such that $f(x_1, x_2, \ldots, x_n) \geq f(a_1, a_2, \ldots, a_n)$ for all $(x_1, x_2, \ldots, x_n)$.

EXAMPLE C.1   Find a relative minimum for the function

$$f(x) = \begin{cases} x^2 + 2x, & x \leq 0, \\ -x, & x > 0. \end{cases}$$

Solution: This function is represented by the curve in Figure C.1. Here $f(x)$ has a relative minimum at $x = -1$, although the function has no minimum.

If now the minimum of $f(x)$ in the closed interval $(-3, 5)$ is requested, the minimum occurs at $x = 5$ and is $f(5) = -5$.

A necessary condition for a relative minimum of a function of several variables is needed more often than a sufficient condition.

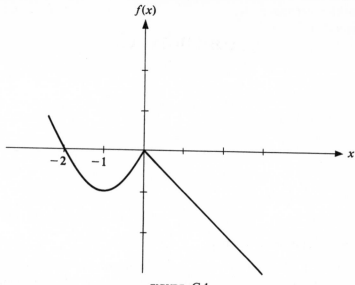

FIGURE C.1

THEOREM C.1 (*Necessary Condition for a Relative Minimum*) If $f(x_1, x_2, \ldots, x_n)$ has a relative minimum at $(a_1, a_2, \ldots, a_n)$, then

$$\frac{\partial f(a_1, a_2, \ldots, a_n)}{\partial x_i} = 0$$

for $i = 1, 2, \ldots, n$.

THEOREM C.2 (*A Sufficient Condition for a Relative Minimum*) If

$$\frac{\partial f(a_1, \ldots, a_n)}{\partial x_i} = 0$$

for $i = 1, \ldots, n$, and if the matrix

$$\mathscr{J} = \begin{bmatrix} \dfrac{\partial^2 f}{\partial x_1\, \partial x_1} & \dfrac{\partial^2 f}{\partial x_1\, \partial x_2} & \dfrac{\partial^2 f}{\partial x_1\, \partial x_3} & \cdots & \dfrac{\partial^2 f}{\partial x_1\, \partial x_n} \\[2mm] \dfrac{\partial^2}{\partial x_2\, \partial x_1} & \dfrac{\partial^2 f}{\partial x_2\, \partial x_2} & \dfrac{\partial^2 f}{\partial x_2\, \partial x_3} & \cdots & \dfrac{\partial^2 f}{\partial x_2\, \partial x_n} \\[2mm] \cdot & & & & \cdot \\ \cdot & & & & \cdot \\ \cdot & & & & \cdot \\[2mm] \dfrac{\partial^2 f}{\partial x_n\, \partial x_1} & \dfrac{\partial^2 f}{\partial x_n\, \partial x_2} & \dfrac{\partial^2 f}{\partial x_n\, \partial x_3} & \cdots & \dfrac{\partial^2 f}{\partial x_n\, \partial x_n} \end{bmatrix} \qquad \text{(C.1)}$$

is positive definite at $(a_1, a_2, \ldots, a_n)$, then $f(a_1, \ldots, a_n)$ is a relative minimum of $f(x_1, x_2, \ldots, x_n)$.

It is not usually easy to prove that a matrix is positive definite. However, one direct test does exist and is as follows: If A is the symmetric matrix

$$\mathscr{A} = \begin{bmatrix} a_{11} & a_{12} & a_{13} & \cdots & a_{1n} \\ a_{21} & a_{22} & a_{23} & \cdots & a_{2n} \\ \cdot & & & & \cdot \\ \cdot & & & & \cdot \\ \cdot & & & & \cdot \\ a_{n1} & a_{n2} & a_{n3} & \cdots & a_{nn} \end{bmatrix} \qquad (C.2)$$

and if the determinants

$$|a_{11}|, \begin{vmatrix} a_{11} & a_{12} \\ a_{21} & a_{22} \end{vmatrix}, \begin{vmatrix} a_{11} & a_{12} & a_{13} \\ a_{21} & a_{22} & a_{23} \\ a_{31} & a_{32} & a_{33} \end{vmatrix}, \ldots, \begin{vmatrix} a_{11} & a_{12} & \cdots & a_{1n} \\ \cdot & & & \cdot \\ \cdot & & & \cdot \\ \cdot & & & \cdot \\ a_{n1} & a_{n2} & \cdots & a_{nn} \end{vmatrix} \qquad (C.3)$$

are all positive, then $\mathscr{A}$ is positive definite.

Appendix D

Inequalities

A topic which is frequently used in error analyses throughout this book is the manipulation of absolute values and inequalities. Some simple properties of absolute values and inequalities are given here without proof or discussion.

Property D.1   If $a \leq b$, then $-b \leq -a$.

Property D.2   If $a \leq b$ and $c \leq d$, then $a + c \leq b + d$.

Property D.3   If $a \leq b$ and $c \leq d$, then ac need not be less than or equal to bd.

Property D.4   If $|a| \leq b$, then $-b \leq a \leq b$.

Property D.5 $|a + b| \leq |a| + |b|$.

Property D.6 $|a - b| \leq |a| + |b|$.

Property D.7 $|a + b| \geq \big| |a| - |b| \big| \geq |a| - |b|$.

Property D.8 $|a - b| \geq \big| |a| - |b| \big|$.

Appendix E

Sequences

A sequence is an ordered set of numbers (that is, a set of numbers which can be put into $1-1$ correspondence with a subset of the positive integers). The sequence $x_1, x_2, x_3, \ldots$ is generally denoted by $\{x_n\}$. The idea of a sequence arises quite naturally in iterative procedures for approximating roots of algebraic equations, among other places. In the case of iterative processes it is desired to find a sequence which is converging to a root of an equation.

Definition E.1 The sequence $\{x_n\}$ is said to converge to the number a if for every number $\epsilon > 0$ there exists a number $N > 0$ such that $|x_n - a| < \epsilon$ if only $n \geq N$.

EXAMPLE E.1 Show that the sequence $\left\{\dfrac{n}{(n+1)^2}\right\}$ converges to zero.

Solution: To show that the sequence converges, it is necessary to show that, for any $\epsilon > 0$, there is an $N > 0$ such that if $n \geq N$, then $\left|\dfrac{n}{(n+1)^2}\right| < \epsilon$. Now $\dfrac{n}{(n+1)^2}$ is always positive for $n > 0$, so that the absolute value can be removed, leaving the equivalent condition

$$\frac{n}{(n+1)^2} < \epsilon.$$

This simply implies that $(n+1)^2\epsilon > n$ or $\epsilon \cdot n^2 + (2\epsilon - 1)n + \epsilon > 0$. But this last inequality is the same as

$$\varepsilon\left(n - \frac{1 - 2\varepsilon + \sqrt{1 - 4\varepsilon}}{2\varepsilon}\right)\left(n - \frac{1 - 2\varepsilon - \sqrt{1 - 4\varepsilon}}{2\varepsilon}\right) > 0. \quad \text{(E.1)}$$

If the two factors in Equation E.1 are positive, then the inequality is assured. Thus, if

$$n \geq N > \frac{1 - 2\varepsilon + \sqrt{1 - 4\varepsilon}}{2\varepsilon} > \frac{1 - 2\varepsilon - \sqrt{1 - 4\varepsilon}}{2\varepsilon}, \quad \text{(E.2)}$$

then $\left| \dfrac{n}{(n + 1)^2} \right| > \epsilon$. For instance, if $\epsilon = 10^{-5}$, then N must satisfy

$$N > \frac{1 - 2 \times 10^{-5} + \sqrt{1 - 4 \times 10^{-5}}}{2 \times 10^{-5}}$$

$$= \frac{10^5}{2} [1 + \sqrt{1 - 4 \times 10^{-5}}] - 1. \quad \text{(E.3)}$$

If $N = 10^6$, this last inequality is satisfied.

Although, in general, it is difficult to determine the limit of a sequence, it is possible in some cases to determine whether or not a given sequence does converge.

THEOREM E.1   If a sequence $\{x_n\}$ is nondecreasing and bounded above, then the sequence converges. If the sequence is nonincreasing and bounded below, then the sequence converges.

By bounded above is meant that there is a number, say a, such that $x_n \leq a$ for all n, while bounded below means that there is a number b such that $x_n \geq b$ for all n.

EXAMPLE E.2   Show that the sequence $\{n/(n + 1)^2\}$ converges.

Solution: Observe that $n/(n + 1)^2 > 0$ for all $n > 0$, so that the sequence is bounded below.   Also, for $n > 0$, $\dfrac{n}{(n + 1)^2} \geq \dfrac{n + 1}{(n + 2)^2}$.   To show this, assume that

$$\frac{n}{(n + 1)^2} < \frac{n + 1}{(n + 2)^2}. \quad \text{(E.4)}$$

Then

$$n(n^2 + 4n + 4) < n^3 + 3n^2 + 3n + 1, \quad \text{(E.5)}$$

and

$$n^2 + n < 1. \quad \text{(E.6)}$$

But since $n > 0$ and integral, then $n \geq 1$ so that $n^2 + n \geq 2$, a contradiction. Thus, as asserted, $\dfrac{n}{(n + 1)^2} \geq \dfrac{n + 1}{(n + 2)^2}$ for all $n > 0$ so that the sequence $\{n/(n + 1)^2\}$ is nonincreasing. Coupled with the fact that the sequence is bounded below, it follows from Theorem E.1 that the sequence converges.

Appendix F

Existence of Solutions for Differential Equations

The numerical solution of ordinary differential equations is considered in Chapter 5. However, an equally important problem is whether a given differential equation has a solution or not. Two conditions are stated here, the first of which guarantees the existence of at least one solution while the second guarantees the existence of a unique solution.

The problem posed is this: Given the differential equation

$$\frac{dy}{dx} = f(x, y), \tag{F.1}$$

is there a solution for Equation F.1 which passes through a given point (x_0, y_0), called the initial condition?

THEOREM F.1 (*Cauchy-Peano Theorem*) If $f(x, y)$ is continuous for some rectangle R defined by $|x - x_0| \le a$, $|y - y_0| \le b$ for a and b real numbers, then there is a solution $y(x)$ of Equation F.1 such that $y(x_0) = y_0$. Further, the solution $y(x)$ and its first derivative are continuous on the interval $|x - x_0| \le \alpha$, where $\alpha = \min\left(a, \dfrac{b}{M}\right)$ and M is the maximum of $|f(x, y)|$ on the rectangle R.

Thus, the continuity of the function $f(x, y)$ in a closed rectangle is enough to guarantee the existence of a solution to $\dfrac{dy}{dx} = f(x, y)$ which passes through the center of the rectangle.

EXAMPLE F.1 Is there a solution of

$$\frac{dy}{dx} = \frac{e^x}{x + y} \tag{F.2}$$

which passes through the point $(0, 1)$?

Solution: Since e^x and $x + y$ are continuous for all values of x and y, their quotient is continuous, provided $x + y$ does not vanish. Hence, the rectangle R must be selected so that $x + y \neq 0$ on R. Thus, if $|x| \leq a$ and $|y - 1| \leq b$, it follows that $-a \leq x \leq a$ and $-b + 1 \leq y \leq b + 1$. Selecting $a < -b + 1$ will guarantee that $x + y \neq 0$ in R. For example, if $a = 0.50$, then $b = 0.49$ is satisfactory.

There is, therefore, at least one solution $y(x)$ of $\dfrac{dy}{dx} = \dfrac{e^x}{x + y}$ which has the property that $y(0) = 1$. The solution $y(x)$ and its derivative $y(x)$ are continuous at $x = 0$.

A further condition, the Lipschitz condition, guarantees that the solution curve $y(x)$, which is known to exist by the Cauchy-Peano Theorem, is the only solution of the differential equation which passes through the initial point.

THEOREM F.2   Let

$$\frac{dy}{dx} = f(x, y) \tag{F.3}$$

with the initial condition (x_0, y_0). Let R be the closed rectangle defined by $|x - x_0| \leq a$ and $|y - y_0| \leq b$. If $f(x, y)$ is continuous on R and for every pair of points (x, y_1) and (x, y_2) in R (notice that x remains fixed) there is a constant K such that

$$|f(x, y_1) - f(x, y_2)| \leq K|y_1 - y_2|, \tag{F.4}$$

then there exists a unique continuous solution $y(x)$ for Equation F.3 over the range $|x - x_0| \leq \alpha$ such that $y(x_0) = y_0$. Here $\alpha = \min\left(a, \dfrac{b}{M}\right)$ and $M = \max|f(x, y)|$ for all points (x, y) in the rectangle R.

The condition expressed by Equation F.4 is the famous Lipschitz condition. It also proves useful as a sufficient condition for the convergence of an iterative process to a root of an algebraic equation (see Chapter 2).

Since it is usually difficult to show that the Lipschitz condition holds in a given case, a second condition, which in turn guarantees that the Lipschitz condition holds, is next presented.

THEOREM F.3   If $\dfrac{\delta f(x, y)}{\delta y}$ exists and is continuous at (x_0, y_0), then the Lipschitz condition is satisfied by $f(x, y)$ in some closed region about (x_0, y_0).

This condition does not give the full information of the previous theorem, but it does give the essential part, that there is a unique solution if there is any solution at all through (x_0, y_0).

Appendix G

Proof of a Statement Following Equation 3.3.6

Given

$$P_n(x) = y_0 + \Delta y_0 u^{[1]} + \frac{\Delta^2 y_0}{2!} u^{[2]} + \cdots + \frac{\Delta^n y_0}{n!} u^{[n]}. \qquad (G.1)$$

To prove

$$P_n(x_k) = y_k. \qquad (G.2)$$

Proof

Since

$$u^{[r]} = u^{[r]}(x) = u(u-1) \cdots (u-r+1)$$
$$= \left(\frac{x - x_0}{h}\right)\left(\frac{x - x_0}{h} - 1\right) \cdots \left(\frac{x - x_0}{h} - r + 1\right) \qquad (G.3)$$

and

$$\frac{x_k - x_0}{h} = \frac{kh}{h} = k, \qquad (G.4)$$

then

$$u^{[r]}(x_k) = k(k-1) \cdots (k-r+1)$$
$$= \begin{cases} \dfrac{k!}{(k-r)!} & \text{for } k \geq r, \\ 0 & \text{for } k < r. \end{cases} \qquad (G.5)$$

Using Equations G.5 and G.1 gives

$$P_n(x_k) = y_0 + \frac{\Delta y_0}{1!} \frac{k!}{(k-1)!} + \frac{\Delta^2 y_0}{2!} \frac{k!}{(k-2)!} + \cdots + \frac{\Delta^k y_0}{k!} \frac{k!}{(k-k)!}$$
$$= y_0 + \binom{k}{1} \Delta y_0 + \binom{k}{2} \Delta^2 y_0 + \cdots + \binom{k}{k} \Delta^k y_0, \qquad (G.6)$$

179

where

$$\binom{k}{r} = \frac{k!}{r!\,(k-r)!}.$$ (G.7)

If each difference in Equation G.6 is replaced by its equivalent in terms of $y_0, y_1, \ldots, y_k$, Equation G.6 can be rewritten as

$$P_n(x_k) = y_0 + \binom{k}{1}(y_1 - y_0) + \binom{k}{2}\left[y_2 - \binom{2}{1}y_1 + \binom{2}{0}y_0\right]$$

$$+ \binom{k}{3}\left[y_3 - \binom{3}{2}y_2 + \binom{3}{1}y_1 - \binom{3}{0}y_0\right] + \cdots$$

$$+ \binom{k}{k}\left[y_k - \binom{k}{k-1}y_{n-1} + \binom{k}{k-2}y_{k-2} + \cdots\right.$$

$$\left. + (-1)^k\binom{k}{0}y_0\right].$$ (G.8)

If, now, Equation G.8 is rearranged by collecting the coefficients of each y_i, the result can be expressed as

$$P_n(x_k) = y_0\left[\binom{k}{0}\binom{0}{0} - \binom{k}{1}\binom{1}{0} + \binom{k}{2}\binom{2}{0} + \cdots + (-1)^k\binom{k}{k}\binom{k}{0}\right]$$

$$+ y_1\left[\binom{k}{1}\binom{1}{1} - \binom{k}{2}\binom{2}{1} + \binom{k}{3}\binom{3}{1}\right.$$

$$\left. + \cdots + (-1)^{k-1}\binom{k}{k}\binom{k}{1}\right] + \cdots$$

$$+ y_m\left[\binom{k}{m}\binom{m}{m} - \binom{k}{m+1}\binom{m+1}{m} + \binom{k}{m+2}\binom{m+2}{m}\right.$$

$$\left. + \cdots + (-1)^{k-m}\binom{k}{k}\binom{k}{m}\right] + \cdots + y_k.$$ (G.9)

But Equation G.9 can be expressed in the form

$$P_n(x_k) = \sum_{m=0}^{k} y_m \sum_{r=0}^{k-m} (-1)^r \binom{k}{m+r}\binom{m+r}{m}.$$ (G.10)

By the definition of Equation G.7,

$$\binom{k}{m+r}\binom{m+r}{m} = \frac{k!}{(m+r)!\,(k-m-r)!}\frac{(m+r)!}{m!\,r!}$$

$$= \frac{k!}{(k-m-r)!\,m!\,r!} \tag{G.11}$$

$$= \frac{k!}{m!\,(k-m)!\,r!\,(k-m-r)!} = \binom{k}{m}\binom{k-m}{r}$$

for $0 \le m+r \le k$.

Using Equation G.11 in Equation G.10 allows Equation G.10 to be written in the form

$$P_n(x_k) = \sum_{m=0}^{k} y_m \binom{k}{m}\sum_{r=0}^{k-m}(-1)^r\binom{k-m}{r}. \tag{G.12}$$

For $m < k$, the terms in the sum $\sum_{r=0}^{k-m}(-1)^r\binom{k-m}{r}$ are the coefficients in the expansion of $(x-y)^{k-m}$; hence the sum is the sum of the terms in the expansion $(x-y)^{k-m}$ for $x = y = 1$; that is

$$(x-y)^{k-m}\Big|_{x=y=1} = \sum_{r=0}^{k-m}(-1)^r\binom{k-m}{r} = 0, \qquad m < k. \tag{G.13}$$

Thus all the terms in the summation of Equation G.12 for $m < k$ vanish, leaving only the term for $m = k$. But for $m = k$, the second summation in Equation G.12 becomes $(-1)^0\binom{0}{0} = 1$. Hence Equation G.12 reduces to

$$P_n(x_k) = y_k\binom{k}{k} = y_k; \tag{G.14}$$

this is just Equation G.2, which was to be proved.

Index

ABCDEFGHIJ   7069876